Scott Peltin & Jogi Rippel – Sink, Float, or Swim

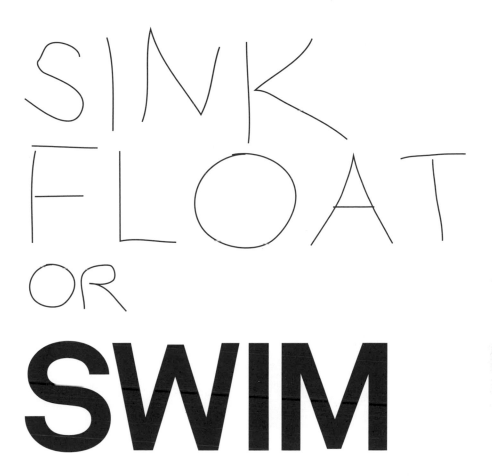

SINK FLOAT OR SWIM

Sustainable High Performance Doesn't
Happen by Chance—It Happens by Choice

Scott Peltin & Jogi Rippel

THIS BOOK IS A LIMITED PRERELEASE.

Bibliographical information from the German National Library

The German National Library registers this publication in the German National Library. Detailed bibliographic information can be retrieved at http://dnb.d-nb.

ISBN 978-3-86881-191-9

www.redline-verlag.de
© 2009 by Redline Verlag, FinanzbuchVerlag GmbH, Munich.

Editor: Christine Buss
Cover Design: Janine Nemec
Book Design: Marko Puclin, Becklyn
Typesetting: Achim Trumpfheller, (Grafik-Schrubber)
Print: CPI – Ebner & Spiegel, Ulm.
Printed in Germany

Prologue

In November 2008, just after the US election, former President Bill Clinton was asked by CNN Talk Asia correspondent Anjali Rao: "If you had to give one piece of advice to offer President-elect Obama, what would it be?"

Clinton paused as he thought carefully, and then he replied that he would tell the new world leader to be sure that he gets enough rest and to invest in his own vitality, so that he can remain as energized, passionate, and focused in the presidency as he was throughout his campaign.

With all the advice that a former world leader could offer another world leader, you may find it surprising that he would choose the suggestion to get enough rest and to invest in his own vitality. Did he offer this advice because he was genuinely concerned about the new President's health? No, that's unlikely. He gave the advice because he knows that energy, passion, and focus are all about performance. They are critical ingredients to being a high performer.

It would be easy to take this as wellness advice, just as it may be easy to categorize this book as a wellness book. But that would be a mistake. This book isn't about politics or about health and wellness. This book is about you, your habits, and your performance. This is a high performance leadership book designed to assist you in achieving your full potential.

We say this with a bias because in our company Tignum, our passion, our expertise, and our mission are all about teaching leaders the importance of having strategies to improve their energy, resilience, brain performance, and capacity so that they can become sustainable high performers.

If you are not familiar with sustainable high performance habits, then you will want to keep reading. If you are familiar with some of these strategies, then you will discover a more integrated approach to build upon the habits you already have. In fact, by the time you reach the end of this book, you will not only understand the importance of sustainable high performance habits, you will have learned some practical strategies for easily implementing these habits into your daily life, both at work and away from work.

Every day, in organizations all over the world, men and women are going to work and using only a fraction of their full potential. They haven't consciously chosen to do this but they have unconsciously done so by their habits. This is costly to the businesses they work for, and it is also costly to their own sense of satisfaction. We have coined the term floater to describe these people, and we have made it our mission to empower the floaters to access their potential and become swimmers.

Of course, we started working with clients to increase their energy and resilience to fight this comfortably numb state long before this current recession hit the world. It was during the good times that we developed these strategies and techniques to help leaders become sustainable high performers. But it is now, in these challenging times, that this book is needed more than ever.

We realize that if you were simply floating before this current crisis hit, you may be dangerously close to sinking right now. But this doesn't mean that it's too late. Every day is a new opportunity for you to eliminate an old low performance habit (like working through lunch or not doing any movement) and replace it with a new high performance habit (like using mental imagery to prepare for a meeting or taking a strategic break to improve your energy and creativity). This book is not so much about how far you've let yourself slide as it is about how you can discover a new potential that you may have forgotten exists.

When we first discussed writing this book, we had reservations about being able to really capture the energy and zeal that is generated when we work with our clients. We understand that translating experiential learning into print isn't always easy or successful. When your passion is improving people's performance and helping them consistently bring their best to everything they do, there's nothing worse than possibly falling short in a book.

We also wondered if it was a smart business decision to share our methodology, given that any competitor could attempt to replicate what we do. Up until now, we have been the performance team behind some extremely productive and successful business teams. Our work has been discussed at length during internal strategy meetings but is relatively unknown to the outside world.

A conversation with one of our clients, an executive board member of one of the largest manufacturing companies in the world, was what pushed us into our decision to write Sink, Float, or Swim. We were sitting in a hotel lobby in London, and he was describing how far his team had come since we had originally worked with them three years prior. He told us that the demands on his team had grown, the pace of the work had increased, and the expectations and need to succeed had exponentially grown but yet his team was full of the energy, vitality, resilience, and capacity needed to meet these challenges. He told us that it was working with Tignum that was the impetus for the positive change in his team's sustainability and performance.

As we finished our green tea (something you'll fully understand when you read this book), he shook our hands, gave us both a hug, looked us in the eye, and thanked us for what we do. Then he smiled and said, "You really ought to write a book. The need is so great and if you really want to impact people's lives, you need to reach farther than just the work you do."

So here we go ...

Put all of your preconceived notions about high performance and leadership aside, and get ready to learn just how easy it is to become a swimmer.

Dedication

This book is dedicated to each and every one of our clients who have allowed us to assist them in achieving their potential. You (especially the cynics) have all inspired us deeply, and we hope that we have represented you well in the stories we have shared.

Section I
Be A Swimmer In A World of Floaters

Quality of Time – maximizing your energy, resilience, brain performance, and capacity to develop sustainable periods where you are fully engaged, passionate, and highly productive at work and away from work

Chapter One
There Is A Swimmer
In All Of Us

Chapter Two
All Good Leaders Must
Learn to Swim

Chapter Three
Without Energy and
Resilience Even Staying
Afloat is Impossible

Chapter Four
Are You Sinking, Floating,
or Swimming?

Chapter One
There Is A Swimmer In All Of Us

At the end of 2008, the CEOs of the Big Three US automakers testified before Congress asking for a $37 billion dollar rescue loan. Congress grilled these CEOs with questions. They asked about their strategies to reinvigorate and innovate their companies. They asked how they were going to retool their plants. They asked how they were going to guarantee the lenders (the US taxpayers) that this considerable loan would ensure that their companies would survive and become profitable again. These were all fair and appropriate questions.

But the questions that they did NOT ask Rick Wagoner, CEO of General Motors, Alan Mulally, CEO of Ford, and Bob Nardelli, CEO of Chrysler, were even more critical to the success of their companies. They should have also asked these leaders important questions about their own individual performance, as well as the performance of their leadership teams:

What are your personal sustainable high performance strategies so we can be assured that you will be able to perform your best during these and future challenging times?

How will you keep your team energized and focused so that they can assist you in inspiring and leading your entire organization through these and future challenging times?

How will you change the culture within your company to support, inspire, live, and breathe high performance?

What are you doing right now to increase your energy and resilience, improve your brain performance, and grow your capacity for the future?

A Recession in Human Potential

We are on the heels of one of the most up-and-down economic years in modern history. The US is in a recession, and the European Central Bank is predicting a similar fate throughout Europe. The German Bank Chief Economist Norbert Walter presented an equally pessimistic prognosis, saying that this could be the biggest crisis since the founding of the country.

But this isn't just a financial recession– it is also a recession in human potential. It isn't just a crisis of a shrinking economy—it is a crisis of shrinking energy, passion, and fortitude of our leadership. We haven't just shrunk the economy. We have shrunk the investment that companies and individual leaders are making, in terms of maximizing the performance of those who must solve the current challenges.

At present, executive burnout rates are higher than ever. Two years ago, 30 to 50% of the global workforce was reported as having experienced occupational stress or burnout. Today, burnout is on the rise across the globe, and in the US alone, it is estimated that occupational stress costs employers in excess of $200 billion per year.

Presenteeism (at work, but not really present) is costing the US over $150 billion annually. Companies are going broke trying to keep up with rising employee healthcare costs. Leaders are distracted from producing results because of low performance habits, fatigue, high stress, and poor health.

It would be easy to blame this recession in human potential on the current economic crisis but this would be incorrect. Over the past 20 years as technology has expanded at a neck-breaking pace, the demands placed on business leaders and executives have exceeded the human physiological capacity to handle it. Simply put, we were not built to handle the way we currently work.

To make matters worse, the current approach to dealing with the side effects of the enormous demands leaders face is also insufficient. There are some excellent medical and wellness programs out there (even though many of these will be the first thing to get cut in tough budget times), but these treat the symptoms of the problem not necessarily the cause. These programs are effective at catching diseases early, educating employees about unhealthy habits, and reducing health insurance payouts; and these things are very important. But we want you to think bigger because just being healthy doesn't ensure that you, or your team, will be high performers.

In the Financial Times, there was an insightful article by Donald Sull entitled, "Why the worst times can also be the best of times." It begins with: "The world has changed. After years of benign economic conditions, the four horsemen of financial apocalypse—credit crunch, recession, volatility, and uncertainty—are blazing a trail across the horizon." The article goes on to describe that this current turbulence creates notable opportunities. Executives, who are poised to capitalize on these opportunities, accelerate change, communicate clearly to an uncertain workforce, and motivate leadership will be the ones to profit greatly.

The problem is—who are these executives? Are they suffering from leadership fatigue or are they energized to thrive? Are they exhausted and overworked from tough budget cuts and shareholder pressures or are they focused, passionate, full of energy, and ready to re-innovate themselves and their companies?

What has made you successful today will not necessarily make you successful tomorrow. Think about what you have to do to remain successful in the future.

| Today | 2010 | 2015 | 2020 | 2025 |

Your Future Performance

The greatest "inconvenient truth" is not that global warming is out of control. The greatest inconvenient truth is that the majority of world leaders, corporate leaders, and executives have no plan to improve their own personal sustainable high performance.

In our work, every time we meet with a group of executives, we ask:

How many people are going to retire in the next two years?
Consistently, no one raises a hand.

How about the next five years?
Usually, no one raises a hand.

How about the next 10 years?
Maybe two people raise their hands.

Is anyone concerned that you won't have the energy to perform at a high level for the next 10 years?
Almost every hand in the room goes up.

Then, we ask:

How many of you have a financial plan for your retirement?
Almost every hand goes up.

Next, we ask:

How many of you have planned for your own personal vitality and health so you can enjoy your retirement?
Again, only a couple of people raise their hands. Team after team, company after company, group after group, and the response is the same.

And then, we ask the toughest question of all:

How many of you feel that you could be better in five years than you are now—that you can have more energy, focus, passion, concentration, clarity, resilience, and capacity in five years?
Not one hand in the room has ever gone up.

This is the saddest moment of all, since the truth is that these things are possible —and even more easily within reach than you can imagine!

Much of the way you perform in the next five minutes is due to the habits you have had for the last three months. Much of how you will perform five years from now will depend on the habits you will begin today. You are a product of your habits, and there is no reason that you can't become a sustainable high performer in all areas of your life within the next three months. It is simply a matter of awareness, choice, and habits.

Let us reiterate this compelling fact:

The way you will perform five years from now will depend on the habits you begin today. You can change your habits today to feel better, have more energy, build greater resilience and capacity, and become a more effective leader five years from now.

A Paradigm Shift

This really is an exciting time to be alive and to be a leader. Martin Luther King Jr. once said, "The ultimate measure of a man [or woman] is not where he [or she] stands in moments of comfort and convenience, but where he [or she] stands at times of challenge and controversy." The question is—what if you have the character and the conviction to handle the crisis, but you're just worn out? Your battery is low, your brain needs more oxygen, your cells are screaming for nutrients, and your doctor has you on medications for sleep problems, depression, hypertension, erectile dysfunction, and ulcers. You've become a side effect of the new corporate world of endless meetings, 24/7 e-mail and text messages, unrealistic shareholder expectations, and the promotion competition to make it to the next level. You are your greatest asset, and your habits will determine if you will fall to mediocrity or rise to your potential. What if the greatest crisis you need to solve is your own energy crisis so you can impact your team, your company, your brand, and your family?

The truth is—you are not alone. We live in a time where there are a multitude of brilliant leadership, business strategy, and financial consultants. There are bookstores full of highly regarded books that provide insights into how to be a better leader, negotiator, or project manager. But what they all miss are the fundamental tools leaders will need to improve their own energy and sustainability.

At Tignum, we believe that you must start with a strong foundation of personal energy, resilience, brain performance, and capacity to become a sustainable high performing leader. This foundation must be in place in order to fully capitalize on all the other effective strategies in leadership and business. This is especially true in these unstable economic times, but it can not be overstated that this is always true.

Why do so many books and business schools miss this essential foundation?

There are many reasons, which we will present later in this book, but the fact is that most people take their own personal energy, resilience, brain performance, and capacity for granted. They wait until a crisis happens before they open their eyes. Even then, they think they are infallible. This paradigm needs to shift. The future isn't about survival—the future is about achieving your potential. We could throw out a million clichés of living life to its fullest, being the best you ... blah, blah, blah ... but you would probably stop reading here.

If you're like the thousands of leaders we have worked with, you want to know that you have an impact. But making an impact in everything you do requires sustainable high performance habits.

The bottom line is:

Do you want to make a difference?
Do you want to enjoy life?
Do you want to leave a legacy?

Hopefully, you aren't too numb or too tired to answer these questions honestly. And, contrary to what you may believe or expect, sustainable high performance is not dependent on huge habit changes; it is built on simple, small changes. This book is about teaching leaders basic high performance strategies. The key, as you will discover in the following pages, is to do these simple things consistently well.

Open Your Mind. Challenge that age-old myth that you cannot be better tomorrow. Plan for your own physical and mental performance and sustainability just as you do for your financial performance. Discover your untapped potential and make the changes in your habits today so that you can enjoy the benefits now, and especially in the future.

Actualize Your Potential

At Tignum, we think the greatest untapped potential of an organization is the performance of their leaders. Within these top players is an amazing ability to inspire, motivate, and ignite the passion and innovation of an entire organization. But in order for this potential to be expressed these leaders must have the energy, resilience, brain performance, and capacity to be their best. This is the foundation of every leader and the foundation of every successful business. If you don't first build a strong foundation for sustainable performance for yourself and your organization, you are risking a collapse.

Sadly, when organizations and leaders preach transformation, innovation, and change, but fail to invest in the sustainability and performance of the leadership and workforce, they are sending a deadly message. They are saying that human capital has minimal value—and they will lose the talent war, the innovation race, and the Darwinian survival challenge. Only companies that spend the time, effort, and money to provide a high performance workplace (with sustainable high performance leaders and workers at the core) will win.

In a recent study by Accenture (a global management consulting, technology services and outsourcing company), intangible assets—such as reputation, intellectual capital, and other non-monetary items—accounted for about 70 % of the value of the S&P 500. This statistic is up from 20 % in 1980. The companies that not only survive the current challenges but thrive in the next decade will be those that master these intangibles.

Every real change, every great company must be built on a strong foundation of energized leaders, a culture of high performance, and a passion for sustainability for the business, the environment, the world, and most importantly, the people. If your people are your organization's greatest asset, then prove it. If you are a leader, then begin by leading yourself first.

Make Your Choice

Play theorist Dr. Brian Sutton-Smith proclaims, "The opposite of play isn't work. It's depression." Furthermore, the opposite of success is not failure—it is living a life where you are comfortably numb. You've seen it. People who get through the day, barely achieving the status quo, who are numb to how low their energy or productivity really is. Even worse, they are unaware of how much unrealized potential they are leaving behind. Then there are those who are energized, passionate, productive, and constantly working to be their best.

Which would you rather be? Are you comfortably numb? Do you have the knowledge, strategies, and habits to be energized, passionate, productive, and sustainable?

Many leaders want to be the energy giver rather than the energy taker, but unfortunately, they are often in survival mode. They think that if they can just make it through this current crisis, they will recommit to some better sustainable high performance habits. However, this is unlikely because there will always another crisis to deal with.

> Seize the Opportunity. The current economy and business challenges require excellence more than ever. There has never been a time when sustainable high performance habits are needed more. The time to develop them is NOW!

There have been economic and financial crises in the 70s, 80s, 90s, and early 2000; and now, in this century, we face the "biggest crisis since the Great Depression," (which lasted from 1929 through the end of the 30s or early 40s for different countries).

The 1973 oil crisis, along with the US stock market crash that lasted from January 1973 to December 1974, affected all major stock markets across the globe. In the 1980s, developing countries across the world faced increasing economic and social difficulties as they suffered from multiple debt crises.

In the US, the savings and loan crisis of the 1980s and 1990s included the failure of 747 savings and loans associations. There was the 1987 stock market crash. And the slowdown in the finance industry and the real estate market may have been contributing causes of the US 1990-1991 economic recession.

In 1992, there was the collapse of the European Exchange Rate Mechanism (ERM) and in 1994, the collapse of the Mexican peso. In 1997, the Thai economy was in crisis with the devaluation of the Thai baht and the collapse of the country's real estate boom.

In this century, there have already been two recessions. There was one from 2001-2003 which affected largely western countries, the European Union in 2001-2002 and the US in 2002-2003, and the second one, which is happening currently. The stock markets in the US, Europe, and Asia have all been affected and show continued volatility.

But, the truth is that in every crisis, there are opportunities. Opportunities for evaluation, for change, for reinvention, for innovation. And there will be many more opportunities in the near future. The only way to survive, have fun while you are doing it, and truly thrive in the future is to become a sustainable high performer.

The critical question is—are you a sustainable high performer?

Chapter Two
All Good Leaders Must Learn to Swim

Sustainable high performance is a condition where you are highly motivated, your self-esteem is strong, your excitement to handle challenges is evident, and your physical energy is abundant. People perceive you as present, grounded, responsive, and focused. You implement sound judgment and innovative solutions, maximizing your impact on your team, company, brand, and the world. Sustainable high performance is showing up consistently with your best game on.

In a 2001 Fast Company interview with Jim Collins, author of Good to Great: Why Some Companies Make the Leap ... And Others Don't, Collins was asked about his research to determine the best way to respond to the economic slowdown.

Collins responded, "If I were running a company today, I would have one priority above all others: to acquire as many of the best people as I could. I'd put off everything else ... to fill my bus. Because things are going to come back. My flywheel is going to start to turn. And the single biggest constraint on growth and the success of my organization ... is the ability to get and hang on to enough of the right people."

This response reflects the belief that it is people (the right people) that lead organizations out of difficult times, and it is these same people that make a company move from good to great (and remain there). And we agree!

However, we would add another foundational element to Collins' approach: You need to make sure that your key people are energized, focused, resilient, passionate, and ready to lead for the duration.

From Good Days to Great Every Day

In a 2007 interview, Matthias Malessa, Chief Human Resources (HR) Officer of the adidas Group, was asked to address the major challenges for HR management. He responded: "Like any good sports team we must recruit talented players, managers and coaches. We need to develop them into a team that trains hard, plays hard and draws on its passion for the game to win. And we need to achieve this in every team, division, function, region ... and brand ... In summary, it's about having the right people with the skills and passion to win in a responsible and fair way."

Again, having the right people is a priority, but even more vital is making sure these people are energized, focused, resilient, passionate, and ready to act in the necessary moment.

We feel, even more so in the present environment, that leaders and A-players need to be sustainable high performers. If they aren't, then even the most talented right people are fractionally functional. Great leaders can occasionally have mediocre performances but when their energy levels drop, their passion wavers, and their focus falters, their entire team suffers.

Any company can survive one bad performer (although when this is an A-player, it can be very costly), but no company can win with mediocre-performing teams. This means that the importance of every leader and A-player being a sustainable high performer is paramount!

Leaders set the tone for the entire company culture. When a leader lives and breathes sustainable high performance, and actively creates a high performance business culture, everything changes. And everyone—shareholders, CEOs, managers, staff, and customers—wins.

There are a wide variety of leadership theories (e.g., transformational leadership, emotional intelligence, authentic leadership) throughout the business world. But there is a common element, upon which all these theories are built. The common element throughout all of these leadership theories is to be the best you—a sustainable high performing, impactful leader. The more self-aware you are, the more you can identify and use your strengths, passions, and abilities to lead yourself, your team, and your organization.

This advice sounds simple but unfortunately, it isn't. It takes an amazing amount of work, energy, and commitment to truly understand yourself, control your emotions, and perform at your best every day. Many times, leaders don't have the energy to do this. Too often, they are just struggling to stay afloat to meet their daily demands.

The Sustainable Success High-Rise

In the competitive business world of today, companies spend a lot of time, energy, and money developing their leaders, focusing on the development of their skills in execution, leadership, communication, project management, negotiation, and time management. Companies address long-term goals and sustainability (usually focused on financial, environmental, and customer base), but they rarely discuss the sustainability of the leaders themselves and of their workforce.

At the heart of leadership in any competitive business are passion, focus, and creativity. These are key ingredients that leaders must have to in order to create winning companies and sustainable high performance results. Passion, focus, and creativity, in turn, require a strong foundation of personal energy, resilience, brain performance, and capacity in order to be truly sustainable.

While many companies may make the fatal mistake of perceiving these as a bonus (if there is enough extra time and money), Tignum sees energy, resilience, brain performance, and capacity as the foundation of sustainable high performance. Furthermore, this sustainable high performance foundation is built on Performance Mindset (covered in Section II), Performance Nutrition (covered in Section III), Performance Movement (covered in Section IV), and Performance Recovery (covered in Section V) habits.

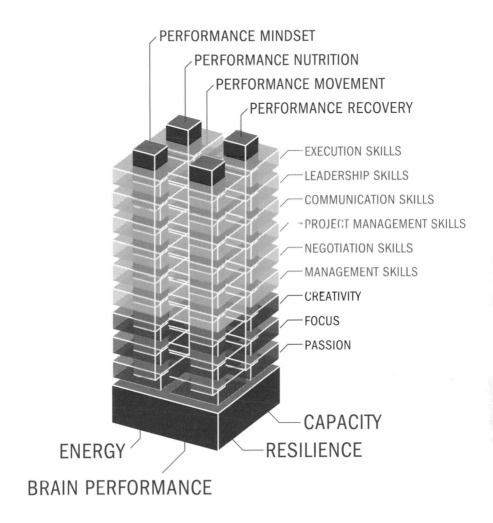

The Tignum Performance Highrise

The Missing Link in Leadership

Clearly, energy, resilience, brain performance, and capacity are vital components to being the best YOU. So if the foundation of all of these leadership theories is a leader's personal energy, resilience, brain performance, and capacity, why are these critical elements so often left to chance? Why do leaders see energy and resilience mostly as parameters of wellness, rather than the foundation of performance? Why is it that CEOs too often see energy and resilience as a nice-to-have rather than a strategic-must? Why do organizations think that a corporate wellness program is enough? Why do organizations think leaders' capacity is an outcome of their genetics rather than an outcome of their habits and environment?

Why don't business schools teach leaders how to develop their personal energy, resilience, brain performance, and capacity?

Why do leaders talk about burnout only after one of their own team members has crashed and burned?

Why don't shareholders and analysts require leaders to develop their own personal energy, resilience, brain performance, and capacity, as well as that of their teams?

There are many answers to all of these questions, which will be covered later, but perhaps the biggest reason that the energy, resilience, brain performance, and capacity of individual leaders is left to chance is that there is a lack of understanding of what sustainable high performance really looks and feels like. Most people don't begin to comprehend how much better they can be.

Perhaps the questions to ask aren't about why this has been missed, but rather why you shouldn't miss it. Ask yourself:

Do you want to come to work awake and energized, passionate about attacking your to-do list, looking forward to the challenges that your day presents, and capable of energizing those around you?

Would you like to attend high performance meetings where all the
participants prepare themselves as well as they prepare their content?
Where people are awake, alert, and full of passion and purpose?
Where the meetings are brief, powerful, and productive?

Would you like to feel the collective energy that is generated by a
high performance team of positive, solution-minded, creative thinkers?
Where negativity is immediately reframed into positive potential and
where, "Yes, let's do it!" is the norm?

Do you want to walk into your home at the end of the day attentive
and focused on those who matter most to you? Where you are engaged
in the family discussions, are happy and enthusiastic, feel playful and
want to have fun? Where you have the energy to be passionate about your
hobbies and to be creative to pursue your dreams?

The answers to these questions are obvious, but do you think your current habits
will get you there?

Power Behind Tignum Strategies

If there is one lesson we have learned at Tignum, it is that there is power^2 in the
total integration of Performance Mindset, Performance Nutrition, Performance
Movement, and Performance Recovery habits. Every day, we speak with clients
who have tried other approaches to improve their energy, resilience, or performance by only addressing one area; and they have failed. They didn't fail because
they didn't try hard enough; they failed because they didn't try smart enough.

TOTAL INTEGRATION OF
MINDSET
NUTRITION
MOVEMENT
RECOVERY®

"I feel like I'm a pretty good performer except during the black-hole hours of 1:30 to about 3:00 pm every afternoon. During this time, I struggle to keep my eyes open. I go to meetings and unless it's a life-or-death issue, I can't focus at all. I find myself craving biscuits, coffee with sugar, anything sweet. I know better, I try to be strong, but I lose my self-control. I try to avoid meetings during this time but that's impossible. In the past two years, I've put on a number of pounds, and this extra weight seems to only make the situation worse."

This is a common story that we hear from our clients. What is the real root of the problem? Is it a sleep deprivation issue? A lack of movement issue? An autonomic nervous system imbalance from too much stress and too little recovery? Or could it be a nutrition issue? The answer is yes to all of these—this all too common problem is almost always created by a combination of issues and can only be solved through a totally integrated approach.

If you are sleep deprived, then your normal afternoon slump will be exaggerated. When this happens, the brain reaches for the quickest source of energy it knows —sugar. Similarly, if you are overstressed, your adrenal glands will struggle to keep you energized throughout the entire day. Under high stress, the elevated cortisol levels tell the brain to crave foods high in sugar, salt, and fat. These are Recovery issues (which will be covered in Section V). If you are eating a lunch with too many calories, too many simple-sugar calories, too little protein, or even too little fat, then your blood sugar levels will certainly dip between 1:30 and 3:00 pm. Your energy will be zapped, and your concentration and productivity will suffer.

If you aren't getting regular movement, especially neurologically stimulating movement, then your brain is not getting the stimulation and oxygen it needs to perform optimally. In addition, as your weight increases, you are moving closer towards adult onset diabetes, hypertension, high cholesterol, and even certain cancers. And, unfortunately, your challenges will only get worse. Fatigue, weight gain, and a feeling of a loss of control can quickly lead to apathy, frustration, and depression.

The downward spiral will continue and trying to solve it by addressing one area simply will not work. The only way to solve a complex problem like this (and not just apply a band-aid) is to use an integrated Mindset, Nutrition, Movement, and Recovery approach. The kicker is that these high performance strategies can be embarrassingly simple, yet when they are done consistently (habitually) and synergistically, the positive results are profound.

Sustainable High Performance Leadership

Although the energy, resilience, or performance you want may not seem achievable right now, we can assure you that it is possible. We have been working with leaders to implement these kinds of high performance strategies, and this is the cornerstone on which Tignum was built.

You can build this enduring foundation through the total integration of Performance Mindset, Performance Nutrition, Performance Movement, and Performance Recovery strategies. These are Tignum strategies that you can easily apply in your busy life every day.

We firmly believe in this approach, seeing firsthand the incredible impact it has had on the companies with which we have worked. We have assisted leaders in looking forward and understanding the requirements for sustainable high performance in a constantly changing world. The following client story exemplifies the results:

"I used to run these three- or four-hour meetings with my team. I remember running straight into these meetings from another meeting. I would be thirsty, hungry, and tired but I just accepted it. During these meetings, we would have some great discussions but when I look back, I realize that there was a lot of frustration just due to impatience from fatigue. We didn't have water for everyone, we didn't have healthy snacks, and we didn't move for hours. It was crazy.

I thought of myself as a good leader but looking back there was no way I was fully energized or very energizing to my team. The eye-opener was that I wasn't aware that I was not at my best. Even worse, I didn't realize that it didn't have to be that way.

Now, my approach is completely different. In addition to preparing my agenda and content for a meeting, I also mentally and physically prepare myself. I see myself as a high performer who is capable of having huge impact if I bring my best game to everything I do. My team really feels the difference.

Now we finish meetings in less time, we get more done, and the team leaves feeling energized and inspired to act."

Consider the following:

What are your current strategies for staying energized and resilient?

What are your current strategies to improve your brain performance?

What are your current strategies to expand your capacity?

How can you build upon these strategies to develop and sustain the self-awareness, passion, focus, and creativity that you need to be the best leader you can be?

Chapter Three
Without Energy and Resilience
Even Staying Afloat is Impossible

When we work with our clients, we ask them to write down their expectations. What would they like to achieve from working with us? Their lists are often long but the common themes demonstrate that leaders want to be more productive (an increase in output) and have a greater impact on their teams, their organizations, their customers, their families, and their communities.

Similarly, they realize that without more energy, resilience, brain performance, and capacity, they will never achieve these goals. They also recognize that once they develop these elements, they will discover an unused potential that is currently dormant.

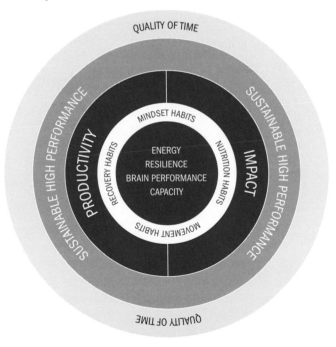

Energy Creates Limitless Possibilities

Our research reveals an alarming trend among executives. Almost all of our clients state that they have less energy at home than they have at work. This means that they burn all of their gas at work and then often go home too exhausted to fully engage in their home life. They don't have the energy to get the satisfaction out of the things that they value the most—their spouse, children, friends, hobbies, and their away-from-work passions.

*"4 Es of Leadership: A high-performing leader has to have positive **energy**—be able to **energize** others—have **edge** (the ability to make tough calls)—and the talent to **execute**. And, passion is the fifth essential trait of leadership."*
Jack Welch, Business Writer and Former CEO of General Electric

Energy is a term that is commonly used but not so easy to define. Positive energy is associated with motivation, exuberance, passion, confidence, and optimism. There is also negative energy which is associated with anger, tension, lethargy, depression, pessimism, and self-pity. There are energy givers and energy takers. There are also many things that give you energy or destroy your energy.

Throughout Sections II to V, we will share numerous Mindset, Nutrition, Movement, and Recovery strategies to help you create more positive energy. We will also give you strategies to reduce your risk for injury and to keep your immune system functioning properly. Injuries or poor health can quickly destroy your energy level. It is easy to underestimate the impact of an injury on your energy level.

How do you currently try to raise your energy level?

What are your energy drainers?

What would you do if you had more energy?

Without Resilience, Failure Is Inevitable

Resilience is the ability to stay focused and passionate about your goals regardless of the normal or unexpected setbacks and challenges. It's the ability to look forward rather than backward, to consciously choose to get up rather than stay down, and to push on rather than give up. Without energy, there is no resilience. Highly resilient people use their temporary setbacks to energize themselves to become more skilled, to do it better next time.

Too often, others may view high performers as always successful at what they do. However, they forget, or don't realize, how many times these high performers have had to pick themselves up from "failures." Michael Jordan, one of the greatest US professional basketball players to ever play the game, best expressed the power of resilience. His response really hits the mark:

"I've missed more than 9,000 shots in my career. I've lost almost 300 games. Twenty-six times, I've been trusted to take the game-winning shot and missed. I've failed over and over and over again in my life. And that is why I succeed."

Jordan's proclamation captures the essence of resilience and its necessity for success, especially in the business world. The fact is that business is tough. Corporate culture isn't always a nice environment. Critics aren't always complimentary. You can't always win. If you want to be a leader, if you want to be an impact player, if you want to participate in solving difficult problems, you will definitely take some hard knocks.

In these challenging times, your resilience is a key component to your sustainable high performance. It is not just pivotal to help you cope with stress and catastrophe. It also enables you to deal with the normal setbacks and frustrations that often come with collaboration, innovation, and problem solving.

Brain Performance for Full Potential

While there is a lot that is unknown about how the brain actually works, it is clear that maximizing your brain performance is essential to achieving your full potential. Your speaking ability, confidence, recall, creativity, and reasoning all impact your success or failure in a negotiation, a presentation, or a strategy-development meeting.

The adult human brain weighs around three pounds (1.36 kilograms) and contains more than 100 billion neurons. It has been called the most complex organ in any creature on earth and it is a computing miracle.

The brain is the center of the nervous system and although it accounts for less than 2 % of a person's weight, it consumes 20 % of the body's energy and 20 % of the body's oxygen. It's made up of approximately 80 % water, and every nerve cell is covered with a myelin sheath (80 % lipid and 20 % protein) that is attributed with the amazing speed in which messages are transmitted.

Nowhere is the total integration of Mindset, Nutrition, Movement, and Recovery habits more important than for your brain performance. In order to perform properly, the brain needs a constant source of oxygen and glucose. Without these two things, it will quickly die.

Adequate sleep is also crucial to proper brain functioning. "One complete night of sleep deprivation is as impairing in simulated driving tests as a legally intoxicating blood-alcohol level," according to Dr. Mark Mahowald, Director of the Minnesota Regional Sleep Disorders Center at the University of Minnesota Medical School.

In addition, the brain needs stimulation to be high performing. More and more research is demonstrating that movement has a profound impact on brain function. Movement improves the oxygen flow, provides neuro-stimulation, and enhances right-and left-brain communication. What's more, the thoughts you feed your brain greatly influence the images it creates and the outcomes produced.

But what if the stimulation is too much or if it is perceived as stress?

Although the body is designed to handle intermittent stress, when the stress is constant and unrelenting, it can have a damaging effect on the brain. Robert Sapolsky, a faculty member in the Stanford Institute for Neuro-Innovation & Translational Neuroscience, has investigated stress and documented that a prolonged flood of stress hormones can actually cause shrinking in certain brain areas, particularly in the hippocampus (which affects your short-term memory and spatial navigation). Sapolsky has demonstrated how constant stress can actually erode memory and the ability to learn. Thus, the key to minimizing the adverse effects of stress is to be sure to get recovery between bouts of stress.

New research is showing that omega-3 fatty acids can help improve brain circulation while high-sugar foods can lead to mood swings, poor decision-making, and sluggishness. The only organ in the body that can't store any of its own energy, the brain is dependent upon specific foods in order to perform optimally.

Dr. Daniel Amen, a leading brain expert, states, "If you don't take care of your brain, you lose an average of 85,000 brain cells a day." This is what causes aging, but with appropriate care and good habits, you can dramatically slow the aging process.

A compelling reason to take care of your brain is to minimize the effects of degeneration (aging and cognitive changes) that happen, as well as to improve your day-to-day performance.

What do you consciously do on a daily basis to improve your brain performance?

Your brain is mostly water—this means that hydration is a necessity. Do you take care to fully hydrate yourself before a must-win negotiation or presentation to enable your brain to function at its full capacity?

Do you strategically select certain foods before an important meeting to ensure that your brain will function at its best?

Left- and Right-Brain Coordination

Scientists describe the brain as consisting of two distinct halves. The left brain is described as the half of the brain responsible for logic, analysis, reasoning, language, math skills, and controlling the right side of the body. The right brain is described as the half of the brain responsible for imagination, creativity, intuition, big-picture thinking, art, music, and controlling the left side of the body.

According to Daniel Pink, author of A Whole New Mind: Why Right Brainers Will Rule the Future, there has historically been a greater value placed on left-brain thinking, but this is changing—and this change will dramatically reshape our lives. Left-brain thinking used to be the driver and right-brain thinking the passenger. However, as we move from the information age to the conceptual age, the use of your right-brain abilities will become more prevalent. Right-brain thinkers who can see the big picture, take the long view, be more empathetic, and maximize their creativity will be the ones to soar in the future.

Chris McManus shares another view with the importance of using your whole brain. McManus writes in Right Hand, Left Hand: The Origins of Asymmetry in Brains, Bodies, Atoms and Cultures: "However tempting it is to talk of right and left hemispheres in isolation, they are actually two half-brains, designed to work together as a smooth, single, integrated whole in one entire, complete brain. The left hemisphere knows how to handle logic and the right brain knows about the world. Put the two together and one gets a powerful thinking machine. Use either on its own and the result can be bizarre, or absurd."

At Tignum, we believe that a high performance brain has to be a coordinated contribution from both the right and left quadrants of the brain. In Section II, we will examine the qualities, attributes, and skills of a High Performance Mindset, and you will see that this requires the collaborative functioning of both sides of the brain.

Creativity Will Rule

When you think about it, in our new world of constant connectivity, we all have access to the same information. You can go to Google, type in the word creativity, and over 62 million sources will come up. Not that long ago, this type of information would be power, but this is no longer the case. This type of information power is now shared by everyone. Or is it?

Kjell Nordström, coauthor of the international bestseller Karaoke Capitalism: Management for Mankind, described it perfectly at a conference in Düsseldorf: "Business today has turned into a karaoke bar. Everything is a copy of a copy of a copy." He explained that it is similar to some untalented drunk patron in a bar singing someone else's original song—business is full of copy-cats. Nordström went on to say that only "imagination and innovation will place societies, organizations, and individuals center-stage."

We wholeheartedly agree with Nordström—creativity is the commodity of the future. Having the information is merely interesting. But taking the same information that everybody else has and doing something unique, useful, and impactful —this will be the ticket for success. At Tignum, we believe this current brain research, along with the focus on creativity, means that a sustainable high performer will need strategies to create a high performance brain that is made up of a coordinated symphony of left- and right-brain functions.

Unfortunately, most executives have no idea how their current habits negatively impact the performance of their brain. They travel across time zones with no strategies to combat jet lag which leaves them fatigued and lethargic, decreases their concentration and focus, and reduces their brain performance. They grab a quick cup of coffee and a cookie as they walk into a meeting to keep themselves awake only to suffer an insulin crash that destroys their memory, creativity, and problem-solving abilities. They take the elevator up one floor to a big presentation, not knowing that walking up the stairs would have oxygenated their brain, as well as improved their ability to think on their feet by stimulating the right brain.

Too often, executives leave their brain performance to chance because they aren't even aware of the impact that their choices have on the brain. At Tignum, we realize that high brain performance doesn't happen by chance—it happens by choice. We teach our clients how to make better choices to ensure that their brain will be performing at its optimal capacity.

What type of choices are we talking about? These are High Performance Mindset, Nutrition, Movement, and Recovery choices that provide the brain with the stimulation, oxygenation, nutrition, and regeneration it needs to perform its best. Even more importantly, it is the total integration of these four pillars of Tignum strategies that will make your brain a sustainable, high performing brain.

Capacity—Is Your Gas Tank Big Enough?

Everywhere in the world, companies are being forced to do more with less. Our clients tell us repeatedly that they are being forced to do two or even three jobs. This shift doesn't just require energy, resilience, and a high performing brain. It also requires a capacity to take on new challenges, to grow, and to become efficient so that you can simply do more.

Traditionally, the lines delineating where one person's area of responsibility stops and another's starts have been black and white. Today, these lines are becoming gray and much less defined. Companies can't afford to keep executives who throw up their hands at every challenge with the response, "That's not my job."

With the current trend of collaboration, both inside and outside of companies, increasing your capacity to take on and meet new challenges is a must. Your potential for growth, power to learn, and ability to perform will be fundamental to the development of your capacity. In athletics, capacity is built progressively through training and practice. In the business world, it is built through the total integration of High Performance Mindset, Nutrition, Movement, and Recovery strategies.

Discover Your Potential

Sometimes acknowledging your potential can be scary. You see that you are settling for less if you don't achieve it, and you also see that much more is possible if you're willing to work to get there. But when you move past your fears, there is nothing more inspiring than having a challenge in front of you that is directly tied to you achieving your own greatness. In a world where mediocrity is often the norm, actualizing potential is rarely discussed, or expected. This is very costly.

In the International Olympic Museum in Lausanne, Switzerland—a beautiful city nestled between the majestic Lake Geneva and the whitecapped Savoy Alps—there is a simple, yet thought-provoking sculpture. Placed among the marble statues of ancient Greek athletes representing grace and sacrifice in sport, this rudimentary form made of one-inch tubular steel portrays another message.

The placard below the sculpture explains that the very small box in the upper right-hand corner represents human lung capacity at rest and the much larger box to the left represents lung capacity during competition. For Tignum, this basic image symbolizes that humankind is functioning at a minute fraction of our potential. At the Olympic Museum, where the greatest athletic feats in history are represented, it is recognized that we all still have an enormous amount of untapped potential.

What untapped potential is lying dormant in you, in your team, and in your organization?

Imagine what a leadership team would be like if every member on that team consistently tapped her/his potential. Imagine the impact that this would have on the rest of the leadership, on the workforce, on the organization, on the brand, and on the consumers. Even more, think about the impact that this would have on your family, your friends, and your legacy. Reaching your potential will generate meaningful outcomes at work and away from work.

So what will it take for you to achieve your true potential?

What do you need to tap into your large box of potential and live there?

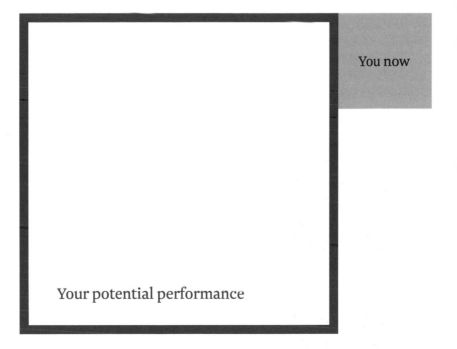

You now

Your potential performance

Too often your habits have left you feeling that you have a greater potential within but you are unable to hold it, to make it happen, to reach it. Unfortunately, you may not be aware of what you repeatedly do.

Did you know that 95 % of your behaviors are unconscious and automatic?

You may be unaware that you repeatedly skip breakfast, drink six cups of coffee to get going, generally walk less than 10 steps before you sit, rarely eat a vegetable, watch TV to fall asleep, or that you consistently play and replay negative thoughts in your mind. Similarly, you may be unaware that you feverishly check your e-mail on your Blackberry during meetings or conversations, or that you rush into meetings late, appearing scattered and unprepared. You are unaware because the brain has an auto-pilot mode that allows you to repeat common patterns without conscious thought.

This paraconscious (between conscious and unconscious) state allows you to perform activities that you are used to doing without attention or thought. An example of this paraconscious state is reading your e-mail on your Blackberry while you're involved in a discussion. You perform this behavior so often that you don't even realize you're doing it. This also means that you are not really communicating because you are not focused on the discussion, you are not fully listening, and you are not effectively dialoguing. You are engaged in the habitual act of multi-tasking, and much of this behavior is not through conscious thought.

The fact is that there are too many executives functioning at a fraction of their potential, and we know that there is a much better way.

Knowing what to do is not enough.

Personal change and achieving personal potential is not just about knowing what to do. It requires action. You have to move from knowing to doing and then do the *right* things over and over again.

All Time Is Not Created Equal

We continually hear from our clients that they don't have enough time. When we inquire further, what they really mean is that they don't have the energy, resilience, brain performance, or capacity to accomplish the results they want to achieve from the time they spend throughout their day.

Clients talk about a meeting being a *waste of time* or their greatest challenge being a *lack of time*. Is it a lack of time or is it a lack of *Quality of Time*? We see *Quality of Time* as a subjective assessment of time spent in your sustainable high performance zone at work or away from work. It's time where you are fully engaged, in the moment, and at your best. It's also a time where you are producing your intended outcomes.

How do you accomplish *Quality of Time*?

Unfortunately, too many executives are just trying to prevent themselves from sinking. They are trying to stay afloat with low performance habits that leave them sick, hurt, numb, or fatigued. In fact, your shelves are probably full of books that you've read but that didn't lead to any significant changes in your life.

We want you to know that this is not another book with wouldn't-it-be-nice stories and bet-you-didn't-know-this headlines. This is a book with strategies that will help you to change your habits, change your energy level, change your productivity, and make your performance at work and away from work truly sustainable. But make no mistake—there is no replacement for ACTION. It is the key to achieving quality of time, high performance, and sustainability.

Sustainable high performance doesn't happen by chance—it's a choice. Every person has the choice to sink, float, or swim.

What will your choice be?

Chapter Four
Are You Sinking, Floating, or Swimming?

After working with thousands of executives, we have found that they fall into one of three categories. They are moving towards a serious crisis (sinking), they are comfortably numb and performing at a fraction of their potential (floating), or they are a sustainable high performer (swimming). We have included a list of characteristics in each category below for you to honestly assess where you are.

Are you a Sinker, a Floater, or a Swimmer?

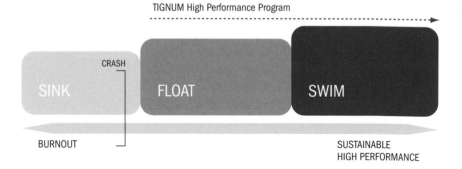

A Sinker ...

_performs at low level of productivity
_doesn't read or recognize body signals (fatigue and sleep
  or digestion problems)
_suffers aches and pains for no apparent reason
_keeps working harder and harder but with less productivity
_struggles with business demands and feels pressured

_has sacrificed relationships for work
_is unaware of unproductive, low performance habits
_ignores personal sustainability until a crisis occurs
_always feels like s/he is one breath away from going under
_does not have a strategy for personal sustainable high performance
_does not see the value in planning for personal performance
_is unaware that Mindset, Nutrition, Movement, and Recovery habits
  impact her/his energy, resilience, brain performance, and capacity

A Floater ...

_performs at a level of mediocrity or unremarkable productivity
_occasionally recognizes body signals (fatigue and sleep
  or digestion problems)
_may have occasional high performance productivity
_uses a lack of time as a common excuse for not investing more
  in personal sustainability
_perceives constant pressure, deadlines, and change processes as
  an endless battle
_prioritizes job sustainability over personal sustainability, sacrificing
  some relationships
_is aware of unproductive, low performance habits, but doesn't
  change them due to limited awareness of performance potential
_believes what brought personal success in the past will lead
  to personal success in the future
_feels like the status quo is as good as it gets
_does not plan for or invest in personal sustainable high performance
_sees sustainable high performance as a nice-to-have rather than a
  strategic-must
_may implement certain performance Mindset, Nutrition, Movement,
  or Recovery strategies but not in an integrated fashion

A Swimmer …

_consistently performs at a high level
_is consciously aware of internal and external signs of being low on gas
_has a high energy level and energizes others
_works smart rather than just hard
_welcomes pressure, deadlines, and change processes but also
 schedules time for recovery and regeneration
_has fulfilling relationships at work and away from work
_continually improves habits and works toward potential
_has great resilience even after setbacks
_feels like life is full of opportunities and is ready to act on them
_plans for and invests in personal sustainability and builds a personal
 vitality profit margin in case a crisis hits
_recognizes sustainable high performance as a strategic-must
_fully integrates and understands that Mindset, Nutrition, Movement, and
 Recovery strategies are the foundation for all performance

While you are at work, do you find yourself sinking, floating, or swimming?

What percentage of the time do you spend in each place?

What about when you are away from work?

"We are what we repeatedly do. Excellence, then, is not an act, but a habit."
Aristotle

Sinking = Burnout

There is one message that comes through loud and clear from every client with
whom we have worked. The demands on them as leaders, managers, team members, husbands, wives, fathers, and mothers are enormous. We always ask the
question: Is your workload greater today than five years ago? And, the answer
is invariably an emphatic YES.

Our clients share that their biggest frustrations come from endless meetings, e-mail overload, and a general feeling of a lack of control over their day. On many days, it takes every ounce of energy they have to keep from sinking.

In addition, most executives have at least one story of someone on their team who is either ready to burn out or has done so already. These very sad stories, and you can feel the impact it has had on the entire team.

In the past 15 years, the rate of burnout has drastically increased. Even more alarming, it is happening to the best performers (not the worst), and at earlier and earlier ages. With the competitive war to get and retain the top talent, and with the growing demands placed on business leaders, A-players crashing and burning out can be very costly.

According to a study by the American Institute of Stress, the estimated costs due to missed work and stress-related illness could be as high as $300 billion annually. In Canada, it is estimated that work-related mental health issues resulted in an annual $3.5 billion productivity loss. In the European Union, it is reported that burnout affects 28% of employees, 38% in the United Kingdom, and possibly even more in the US.

Findings from the Hudson Burnout Britain Report (2005):
_More than half (52%) of Britain's employees claim to have experienced one or more symptoms of over-work or burnout in the last six months.
_One in two employees (49%) and employers (46%) thought the situation had worsened in the last five years.
_Employees (76%) and employers (78%) were most likely to believe that the increased pace of business life was a cause of burnout.
_One in seven (14%) of the HR managers interviewed have lost one or more members of staff due to burnout.

With the economy worsening, competition increasing, and the demands placed on executives rapidly growing, can a company really afford to have this many people sinking? Burnout doesn't just impact the bottom line—it impacts the company morale, the organizational culture, the productivity, and ultimately the shareholder value.

In the Scientific American Mind, Berlin science writer Ulrich Kraft describes the *burnout cycle* and why it has become so prevalent. He notes that part of the quicksand of burnout is that it doesn't happen overnight—it develops gradually over time. The cycle actually begins with a compulsion to prove oneself, an expectation that any high performer embraces. Then, as personal high expectations continue to grow, people take on more and more work to support their inner notion of *irreplaceability*. Finally, they take the plunge that often leads to their own sinking: they dismiss their own needs for critical elements like sleep, exercise, food, friends, or fun. This self-sacrifice is often perceived as the final proof of heroic performance.

Interestingly enough, Dr. John Sarno, from the NYU Langone Medical Center, also describes this *perfectionist* type of personality as the greatest at risk for low back, knee, and shoulder pain. In his book The Mindbody Prescription: Healing the Body, Healing the Pain, he also associates other common health conditions such as fibromyalgia, asthma, and arthritis to the psychosomatic onset of a condition called tension myositis syndrome (TMS). TMS causes a condition of oxygen deprivation in the tissues which he attributes to the pain, most notably back pain.

At Tignum, we believe there is another way—a new way of working—utilizing effective High Performance Mindset, Nutrition, Movement, and Recovery strategies to access your potential and sustain your performance. Our goal, and passion, is to help every person move towards becoming a sustainable high performer. We can assure you that sustainable high performers are not born this way. They are people who have committed themselves to doing simple things consistently well in order to actualize their potential.

Burnout is the result of constant and persistent stress without adequate recovery to rebalance your autonomic nervous system (ANS). The ANS controls involuntary activities in your body such as heart and respiration rates, digestion, perspiration, urination, and sexual arousal.

There are numerous factors that contribute to burnout such as a lack of control of the work environment, unrealistic expectations, perfectionism, a bombardment of critical decisions (especially those that negatively impact the lives of others), and a non-supportive work culture. But burnout is not an absolute. Some people appear to be less resilient to burnout than others, and this resiliency can be developed.

Physical signs of burnout: lack of energy, inability to get up to come to work, lack of concentration, insomnia, aches and pains, physical exhaustion, forgetfulness

Emotional signs of burnout: frustration and general irritability, feeling isolated, emotionally drained, cynicism, despair, apathy, withdrawn, sense of helplessness, and hopelessness

Burnout is a serious medical condition and can lead to suicide. If you believe you are suffering from burnout, you need to seek medical attention and the care of a qualified psychological and medical team.

"The last act of the stress cycle, burnout is a fitting epidemic for the overwork age. Its total colonization of the mind, body, and spirit mirrors the complete takeover of life by the job."
Joe Robinson, American Consultant and Author of Work to Live: The Guide to Getting a Life

Floating = Comfortably Numb

Yet, this tells only one part of the story. There are rising catastrophic burnout rates, but in addition to this alarming trend, there are also a large percentage of executives that are simply trying to stay afloat. This means they come to work every day, they do their best to achieve the status quo, and then they go home exhausted hoping that tomorrow will be a better day. They are treading water in the middle of a vast ocean of expectations, increasing business challenges, reduced resources, and greater short-term demands, without any glimpse of a rescue boat or the shore.

Although there are statistics that attempt to estimate the productivity loss due to burnout, there aren't any measurements of the cost of mediocrity from a large part of your workforce just trying to stay afloat. These are the comfortably numb leaders who have lost sight of what high performance looks like, feels like, and smells like. Even worse, they don't realize that life can be better. They suffer compassion fatigue which destroys the energy, productivity, and culture of high performance teams.

In an October 2004 article in the Harvard Business Review, Paul Hemp defined presenteeism as the problem of being on the job but, because of illness or other medical conditions, not fully functioning. The productivity loss due to presenteeism in the US alone is estimated to be $150 billion which is far more costly than absenteeism. Unlike absenteeism, the problem with presenteeism is that it isn't always apparent. People are at their desk, appear to be fine, but inside they may be struggling with common ailments like allergies, headaches, arthritis, back pain, depression, or some other performance-hindering condition. Side effects of the medications they are taking may also challenge and adversely affect their performance.

Average number of unproductive hours in a typical 8-hour day

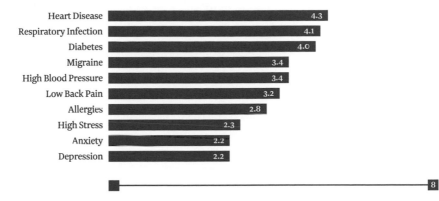

Adapted from a study done by Cornell University Institute for Health and Productivity Studies (IHPS)

Although the study of presenteeism is still young, it is our opinion that these statistics are an underestimation of the true cost of pain and illness. For example, researchers from Tufts New England Medical Center in Boston reported that the incidence of chronic lower back pain was 21.3 % and depression only 13.9 % in the Lockheed Martin study. In our medical evaluations, we have found that closer to 50 % of executives suffer from consistent lower back pain, and the depression rates (especially those who don't take medications) are also far higher. Even more frightening, there is an unknown percentage of executives who self-medicate, which surely impacts their productivity and performance.

Another confounding factor to actually being able to measure the true impact of presenteeism is the veil of secrecy that surrounds illness (especially mental illness). We have had clients confide that they have suffered medical maladies (even heart attacks) and never shared this information with their bosses or with their company physicians.

Even further complicating the true cost of presenteeism is the fact that most executives don't get regular medical examinations, and they are often unaware of underlying potential medical problems. In almost four years of testing executives for our programs, we have found that 40% of our clients have hypertension and 38% have abnormal blood results, and they had no prior knowledge of these conditions. This has been a huge wake-up call for Tignum and for our clients.

Do you know your blood pressure? Do you know your cholesterol level? Do you have allergies? Do you regularly suffer from knee, back, or shoulder pain? What medications do you take? What are the side effects of these medications? When was your last medical examination? What do you do every day to prevent illness, injury, or chronic pain? What do you do every day to strengthen your immune system? Are your current habits leading you towards being one of these statistics?

Mindlessness = Status Quo

In today's world of business with downsizing, buyouts, constant reorganization, and rapid change platforms, the emotional demands placed on managers and leaders are growing exponentially. When examining current leadership habits, Richard E. Boyatzis and Annie McKee, in their book Resonant Leadership: Renewing Yourself and Connecting with Others Through Mindfulness, Hope, and Compassion, also found that if leaders were focused only on results, they often slipped into "a state of mindlessness." This mindlessness takes a toll on leaders both physically and emotionally. It creates floaters of the best leaders in the short-term and makes personal sustainability impossible in the long-term. Eventually, this can lead to leaders who can no longer motivate themselves or their teams to be creative and productive, which can severely wound the spirit of the company. In a competitive world, this is how companies lose their competitive edge.

Whether or not these leaders actually suffer heart attacks, their companies will eventually suffer shareholder-value strokes; and the profitability of the companies will be paralyzed. The reality is that business can be tough and even cruel sometimes, and often only the strong survive. In a tough economy, the smart money is on the leaders who realize that the corporate culture must be in place to improve the energy, resilience, capacity, and sustainability of every person in their company.

It's interesting to note that many Fortune 100 companies have a policy that the executive leadership team can never travel together in the same airplane. This way, in the case of a catastrophic crash, the company will not lose all of its leaders or its continuity. This policy implies that there is a high value placed upon these key leaders, their contributions to the company, and the importance of them being able to come to work.

If companies go to such lengths as to require that their top leaders not travel together, why don't they insist on a company culture built on sustainable high performance? We asked one of the leading international business gurus and bestselling authors, C.K. Prahalad, about some of these important issues.

Why do you think so many leaders see their personal sustainability (energy and resilience) as a nice-to-have rather than a strategic-must?

Prahalad: Most of these executives and CEOs start in these companies when they are young. When you're young you feel invincible—even if you're not. However, just because you can cope doesn't mean you are at your best. You don't know how good you could be, and people won't tell you when you're not at your peak. In addition, there are companies that invest in the health of their leaders and workforce, but good health does not translate directly to high performance. The mindset is the key.

It seems that in tough budget times, employee development and high performance programs are often the first to get cut. What are your thoughts on this approach?

Prahalad: It's unfortunate and a knee-jerk reaction. It's a mistake and demonstrates very short-term thinking. I encourage leaders not to take this approach— not to cut this type of vital leadership development. When they make these kinds of cuts, they will surely pay for it later.

Why are you committed to your own personal sustainable high performance?

Prahalad: The reason I am so committed to my sustainable high performance is that my work requires much international travel, and there is always the expectation that I am ready to go when I land and that I'll be highly focused. When I work with a company, I must be alert for long periods of time. I have multiple roles as an academic, a writer, and a consultant. My job requires that I'm mentally alert and physically fit.

Clearly, C. K. Prahalad is a swimmer.

Companies often fail to build a culture of high performance because of their lack of awareness. When you are comfortably numb, you don't always know how bad you may be or how good you could be. You've probably seen glimpses of your potential, but you've never gotten to swim in it so you could really enjoy the benefits. You may not associate Mindset, Nutrition, Movement, and Recovery habits with your business performance. Instead, you may associate these strategies with wellness, health, or physical appearance, and then wait for a performance or health crisis before you do anything about your personal habits.

Wellness Programs ≠ High Performance

This lack of awareness also contributes to the wellness program trap. Too often, CEOs assume that if they have a company wellness program, everyone must be well. This false assumption usually goes hand in hand with the assumption that if the leaders and the workforce are well, they must be functioning at full capacity.

Unfortunately, these assumptions cloud the real picture of performance:

_Annual checkups identify illness—they don't prevent them.
_Corporate fitness centers are most used by those who are already fit.
_Presenteeism makes it look like everyone is well, but this
  is often not the case.
_Everyone is not an athlete and "exercise" is not for everyone.
_Wellness programs are designed to help people stay afloat,
  to prevent them from sinking, but not necessarily to help them become
  sustainable high performers.

Wellness and health are definitely components of sustainable high performance, but alone, they do not lead to high performance.

Swimming = Sustainable High Performance

Sustainable high performance is a condition that occurs when a person is stretched beyond her/his comfort zone but not beyond her/his skill level. It is a condition of high energy and passion, low anxiety, and maximum productivity. It is not a one-time experience but rather a normal state where mediocrity is unacceptable but perfection is not the objective. It is a condition that yields high motivation, strong self-esteem, excitement to handle challenges, and abundant physical energy. Sustainable high performance is an outcome of excellent habits. It is a process and not a destination.

Three years ago, one of our clients, Sandy Ogg, the Chief HR Officer of Unilever, recognized that he and his team were struggling. He described that they were facing insurmountable challenges and they were doing everything they could to just stay afloat. This wasn't a knock on himself or his team. Rather, it was a by-product of the enormous demands they were facing along with their current habits.

At one of our meetings, Ogg stood up in front of his entire team and shared his desire to become a swimmer. He told the group he knew it would require some personal changes, but that he wanted to be a good example to everyone and to improve his own sustainable performance. Since then, like all of us, he hasn't been perfect, but he has purposefully adopted a variety of sustainable high performance habits.

He awakens every morning with a commitment to his own personal energy, resilience, brain performance, and capacity. His morning starts with some movement and a high performance breakfast. Next, he looks at his daily agenda, and spends a few minutes setting his intentions and mentally preparing for his day. He envisions his day as a series of performances, all of which will require his full attention, energy, focus, and passion.

Once at work, Ogg prepares his brain for optimal performance (with the proper thoughts, movement, and nutrition) before each meeting. He takes a few minutes before to set his intentions and a few minutes after each meeting to debrief. He understands that in each and every interaction he has, there is the potential to impassion and energize company leaders or leave them flat, uninspired, and feeling insignificant.

Do all of these strategies take a lot of time and energy?

Not really—because it's a routine, a set of daily habits. Ogg understands that his hectic schedule, relentless travel demands, and challenging workload can, at any moment, drag him back into being a floater. But he keeps focused, by having good sustainable high performance habits, because he has made the choice to be a swimmer.

Is he perfect with these habits every day? No way. But he is committed. And part of being a swimmer is realizing that every day is a work in progress. Every action you take will either help you swim or make you sink.

Personal Performance = Company Profitability

In a 2007 Fast Company article, Yuval Rosenburg looked at an evolving trend of investment groups to examine not just short-term returns but also sustainability. One such group, HIP Investor, Inc., has defined the practice as Human Impact + Profit (HIP)™. HIP is a quantitative measurement of how a company treats the environment, its employees, its customers, and the community. HIP Investor founder and CEO R. Paul Herman shared with us: "We want to measure how a company's management approach drives human impact and how that human impact drives higher profit. To do this, we look at the impacts (health, wealth, earth, equality, and trust) of both customers and employees, the impact on the environment, and the impact on social equality. Clearly, we can see that the culture the leader sets pervades the entire organization. We suspected that a company could do the right thing in the short-term (for their employees, customers, and the environment) and still be very successful in the long-term, and the HIP Index's metrics and financial outperformance prove that concept in real life. We were right."

This type of approach is in its early stage, but HIP is revolutionary, certainly pushing the envelope in linking the health and well-being of a company and its leadership approach directly to the long-term profitability of the enterprise.

This focus on the health of company leadership is also reflected in The Huffington Post headline, "Apple Shares Fall on Steve Jobs Health News." In this article, Jessica Mintz wrote: "Apple's stock has surged and tumbled over the last year in step with rumors or news about the CEO's condition. While the top executive's health is an issue for investors of any company, at Apple the concern reaches fever pitch because Jobs has a hand in everything from ideas for new products to the way they're marketed."

While Steve Jobs is certainly not just any CEO, and the ethics of speculators having access to personal medical information is questionable, the point is that the health and well-being of the CEO and top leadership always matters. In fact, we believe that when companies invest in the sustainable high performance of their leaders, it should be heralded as good for the company, good for the employees, and good for the investors.

Is More Energy Enough?

One of our favorite video clips is of a well-known CEO energizing his company's leaders. It shows him bouncing, skipping, screaming, and cheering as he energizes the crowd. They are clapping, cheering, and egging him on. You can see that they love their leader and the energy he is inciting in them. The video clearly shows his passion and his intention for honoring the company and his workforce.

Afterwards, the fatigued CEO leans on the podium as he catches his breath, the effort and the excitement of delivering such an energetic entrance evident. At this point, we always ask the question: Is this high energy? Of course it is. Then we follow it up with:

Is it sustainable?

We are inspired by this CEO's passion for his company, his effort to energize himself and his employees. In the video clip, he emphatically states four words: "I love this company!" However, even with his tremendous love for his company, will this CEO have the energy and resilience to sustain his personal performance?

When we address sinking, floating, or swimming, we are talking about men and women who love their companies, love their jobs, love their teams, love their spouses, and love their children. But, the reality is that when they sink, everyone suffers.

"Your first and foremost job as a leader is to raise your own energy level and then to help raise and orchestrate the energies of those around you."
Peter Drucker, Austrian Management Consultant and Social Ecologist

The Rise of "Extreme Jobs"

Sylvia Ann Hewlett and Carolyn Buck Luce published a compelling article in the Harvard Business Review on the dangerous allure of extreme jobs. Their research in this area is based upon two surveys: one focusing on "high earners in various professions across the US" and the other targeting "high-earning managers in large multinational corporations." In addition to the surveys, they gathered information from 14 focus groups and 35 one-on-one interviews. Hewlett and Luce defined extreme jobs utilizing the following criteria:

"For the purposes of data analysis, we've said that survey respondents have such jobs if they work 60 hours or more per week, are high earners, and hold positions with at least five of these characteristics:

_unpredictable flow of work
_fast-paced work under tight deadlines
_inordinate scope of responsibility that amounts to more than one job
_work-related events outside regular work hours
_availability to clients 24/7
_responsibility for profit and loss
_responsibility for mentoring and recruiting
_large amount of travel
_large number of direct reports
_physical presence at workplace at least ten hours a day"

Using this definition, they identified that 21% of those surveyed in US companies and 45% of those working in global companies had extreme jobs. When asked why they did these extreme jobs, 90% of male and 82% of the female respondents stated that their jobs were stimulating and challenging, and their work gave them an adrenaline rush. The graph below highlights some of the other reasons people gave.

Why Do You Do it?

Holders of extreme jobs indicated what motivates them to work long, stressful hours. They answered the question "What are the main reasons you love your job?" Multiple responses were allowed.

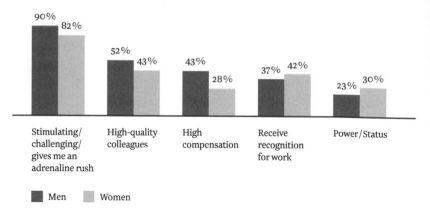

Men   Women

Hewlett and Luce also noted that "extreme jobs are no longer a rarity." This study was completed in 2006, and with our current economic demands, it is important to acknowledge that today, extreme jobs are more prevalent than ever before.

The truth is that just as there has been a rise in extreme sports, there will always be an allure for certain individuals to do extreme jobs. There will also be certain work cultures that recruit for, and brag about, their extreme work environments. Is this okay or is this wrong? This is not for us to judge because it is a personal choice that people make, and we respect that.

The better question—as Hewlett and Luce asked—is it sustainable?

Whether you choose an extreme or regular job (which, today, is looking more and more extreme), we recognize that you are always seeking to reach your potential, to become a sustainable high performer.

If you sink, it is a tragedy, impacting a wide spectrum of life. It is a business tragedy that will impact your co-workers, your team, and your company. And, it is also a personal tragedy since it impacts your spouse, your children, and your personal community.

"The first time I saw a presentation about Tignum, I was intrigued. For the six months leading up to that day, I had been struggling with burnout. Just two months before, I had gone to my doctor because I was exhausted, couldn't focus, couldn't sleep, and couldn't even remember my assistant's name. My doctor diagnosed me with acute burnout, put me on sleeping pills, and told me to stop doing all exercise and work for three weeks. This forced check-out was then extended an additional two weeks. When I started working with Tignum, I had been back to work on a part-time basis for just three weeks. It was hard to say that I was back to work, though, because it wasn't really me, and I wasn't really productive.

I was most interested in Tignum's total integration approach. It was so different from what my doctor had prescribed. When I showed up for my pre-Tignum program evaluation, my hands were shaking and I was so nervous, not because I was afraid, but because my system was so out of balance.

As I proceeded with the different tests, the Tignum staff asked me specific questions about my burnout: Had my doctor talked to me about my mindset and how to manage my thoughts? Had he had suggested any nutritional strategies to rebalance my autonomic nervous system? Had he recommended some regenerating movements such as yoga, tai chi, qigong, or stretching? Finally, they asked me if the doctor had given me any relaxation, breathing, or sleep techniques.

For a split second my shaking stopped as I grinned and emphatically said, "No, he recommended none of these." I don't have to tell you that, in that moment, I realized that the Tignum approach was unique. For the first time, I really felt like there was hope. Hope that I would get well and even more importantly, hope that I could regain my old high performance ways.

I won't tell you it has been easy, but I will tell you that once I consistently implemented Mindset, Nutrition, Movement, and Recovery strategies, I started to feel better. It took me a year, but my hope has turned into positive results. I can tell you that I'm back to a top leadership role, and every day I do something for my own sustainable high performance. I've learned my lesson of not making my own energy and resilience a priority and finally, I am excited about my future."
Tignum Client

At Tignum, we unequivocally believe that every solution must be a total integration of Mindset, Nutrition, Movement, and Recovery strategies. The brain requires high performance nutrition, hydration, and energy to function optimally. It also needs oxygen and neurological stimulation that can only come from consistent movement. In addition, the brain needs rest and regeneration to solidify memory and replenish vital brain chemicals. Finally, when your mindset is optimistic, solution-oriented, confident, focused, creative, and passionate, anything is possible. The mind and body are intractably linked, and one needs the other to achieve sustainable high performance.

It is important to note that the Tignum system is not a medical or health program—our system is based upon a high performance approach. It is the total integration of Performance Mindset, Performance Nutrition, Performance Movement, and Performance Recovery strategies done habitually to improve energy, resilience, brain performance, and capacity to achieve sustainable high performance. This is the Tignum approach, and our clients have proven that it works.

Do you have strategies that give you energy, resilience, capacity, and high performance when you need it?

Will your current habits get you where you need to be tomorrow?

Section II
Getting Your Head Above Water

Performance Mindset – positively focusing on and developing your thoughts, beliefs, attitudes, and vision to improve cognitive and creative aptitude and produce sustainable success

Chapter Five
What Is a High Performance Mindset?

Chapter Six
Create Your High Performance Mindset

Chapter Seven
Expand and Sustain Your High Performance Mindset

Chapter Five
What Is a High Performance Mindset?

"Every day, I come into work with what I think is a very positive mindset. I feel like I'm happy and relaxed, but before I know it, I feel like my job has sucked the life out of me. I become negative and unable to perform my best. I often feel like the ball in a tennis match, and I'm being hit back and forth with no control."

You may identify with this Tignum client's experience. Unfortunately, this is common for too many executives. In every program, we begin our Mindset discussion with this client experience and although everyone laughs, they also cringe at the same time. We get this response because people can relate to the challenges that seem to permeate their greatest intentions of staying positive.

What are the things in your day that contribute to the destruction of your positive Mindset?

What things wear on you, knock you off your game, drain your energy, and take away your ability to stay in a High Performance Mindset?

Consistently, the answers we receive in response to these questions include things like the traffic, weather, the commute, rude people, constant deluge of e-mail messages, unrealistic expectations, too many or unnecessary meetings, constantly changing priorities, personality conflicts, delayed flights, long security lines, negative people in the office, money problems, and office politics. This list is long but it is definitely not all-inclusive. You can probably add a few items of your own to it.

We realize that this may seem like a negative beginning to a very positive topic, but we feel it is necessary. This is an awareness exercise and becoming aware of the negative thoughts that you have which impact your Performance Mindset is critical.

Define a High Performance Mindset

What is a Performance Mindset? Is it something you can describe? Is it something you have experienced? Do you know a High Performance Mindset when you see it? Is there a person (a colleague, a leader, an athlete, a politician, a relative) that demonstrates what you consider to be a High Performance Mindset? What are the qualities, attributes, and skills that you want in your High Performance Mindset?

The more detailed your answers to these questions, the more meaningful your High Performance Mindset. This is a significant part of developing a clear picture of what you want your Mindset to become.

Throughout the work we have done with high performers, we have developed a consistent (but not necessarily comprehensive) list of the qualities, attributes, and skills that are necessary for creating this kind of positive Mindset. These components always lead to great discussion, so we have included a sampling to stimulate your Mindset list:

positive attitude

creativity

concentration

optimistic outlook

vision

control of emotions   fun

goals

discipline   resilience

focus

confidence

solution-oriented approach

flexibility   action-oriented approach

plan

Concentration

The number of interruptions that people experience in the workplace is immense. This fact has led to a new field of study called interruption science. During an interview with BusinessWeek, Maggie Jackson, the author of Distracted: The Erosion of Attention and the Coming of the Dark Age, stated that the average American knowledge worker is disrupted once every three minutes and tends to stay an average of 11 minutes on one project. Jackson said studies by Gloria Mark and others show that once interrupted, the average worker takes 25 minutes to return to their original task.

Interruption science is an emerging field that studies the effect of disruptions on job performance. This new science is not surprising when you consider these statistics: 1 million IM messages sent every second, 2 million e-mails sent every second, 100 billion clicks on the internet each day.

According to recent research in this area, this constant interruption leads to an estimated productivity loss of $650 billion a year for US businesses, alone. Clearly, the need to develop an environment and tools for concentration is fundamental to creating your High Performance Mindset.

Control of Emotions

Have you ever watched an extraordinary athlete such as Steffi Graf play point after point in a big match, appearing almost emotionless? How about Tiger Woods as he sinks a winning 25-foot putt to capture a major championship? Suddenly, the second the match is over, the gates open and these athletes collapse in tears of joy. Where did these emotions suddenly come from? Just a second ago, these high performers appeared so inhuman. The fact is that it is impossible (unless there is a pathological condition) to not feel some emotion. The challenge is to control your emotions, when acting them out may not be conducive for high performance. What if you're feeling anger, frustration, or dissatisfaction, but you know that exhibiting these emotions will destroy the trust or energy of the group? Learning to control your emotions (not deny or eliminate feeling your emotions) is a fundamental component to a High Performance Mindset.

Creativity

Just 10 years ago, creativity would probably not have made it onto this list. It may have been preempted by knowledge (of business, competitors, and customers). But as we previously discussed, creativity really is the commodity of the future. In fact, we rarely lead a Mindset discussion where someone doesn't mention creativity and the rest of the group doesn't enthusiastically shake their heads in agreement. Creativity is, and will continue to be, integral to business problem-solving and success.

Resilience

The road to success is definitely not linear. There are many ups and downs, and the ability to rebound from setbacks, bad news, and failure is crucial. A High Performance Mindset cannot be kept down. Most high performers don't perceive setbacks or failures as negative. They are so resilient that they see them as steps on a staircase to achieving their ultimate goals and fulfilling their vision.

Optimistic Outlook

This attribute commonly comes up in our discussions, eliciting lots of passionate debate about the place for pessimism in a High Performance Mindset. Great leaders can't always be optimistic, because the facts must speak for themselves. Although there is a positive relationship between being optimistic and being resilient, there is also a solid argument for being pessimistic and thoroughly questioning the assumptions or objectives. In order to create your High Performance Mindset, you need to develop an authentic optimism that high performance is indeed achievable and that the problem at hand can be solved.

Positive Attitude

One attribute that always comes up in our discussions is a positive attitude. Nothing destroys an individual's and team's energy like a negative attitude. Whether it's a business team, a project team, an athletic team, or a firefighting crew, when one member (especially if it's the leader) has a negative attitude, everyone suffers. For this reason, maintaining a positive attitude is paramount in developing your High Performance Mindset.

Fun

Too often, developing a High Performance Mindset is seen as all work and no fun. This is a big mistake and can often lead to frustration. Human beings are wired to seek enjoyment, and when you make your own personal innovation a fun experience, you are far more likely to succeed. Finding enjoyment in your own personal innovation is critical. Laughter is also an essential component of our Recovery system, and the Mindset benefits of fun are added value.

Goals

It goes without saying that goals are important to achieve anything. But as we will discuss later, too often motivation is lost by writing long lists of unemotional, uninspiring, dull goals. On the flip side, when you develop meaningful, fun, and passionate goals, you will find it much easier to remain disciplined.

Vision

A clear, detailed, sensory-rich vision is probably one of the most important, and often overlooked, components of a High Performance Mindset. How can you go into a board meeting and project confidence and conviction if you can't even see yourself with those attributes? Learning to see yourself with a High Performance Mindset is one of the first and most powerful steps to making it a reality. We will help you work on developing your vision later in this section.

Plan

All the goals in the world won't come to fruition if you don't have a concise, positive, and doable plan. Even the great Adidas catch phrase, Impossible Is Nothing, cannot happen without a well-developed game plan. Without a plan, you are leaving your success to chance, and that's no way to become a sustainable high performer.

Discipline

Without a doubt, discipline is an important element in developing a High Performance Mindset. Discipline is not about being hardheaded but is more about the ability to do the right things even when you don't want to. Discipline is having the self-control to do what is necessary to prepare and plan for the many variables in any situation. One area that many executives overlook is the discipline to individually prepare themselves mentally, physically, and emotionally before they need to perform (at work and away from work).

Confidence

No one has ever reached their full potential in becoming a high performer without being self-confident. But what happens when your confidence wavers? Have you ever prepared for weeks for a presentation only to have your confidence crash the night before? Suddenly, you may find yourself full of doubts, unable to quiet your negative self talk, and nervous about the consequences of failing. Although this is a completely normal response, there are strategies that can be used to quickly turn this Mindset around. We will cover some of these later in this section.

Focus

Focus is not something you have or don't have. Focus is a skill that can be learned and practiced. It is the development of your ability to concentrate strategically on the issue at hand, moving effectively from a wide to narrow perspective, or from an inner to outer perspective, as required by each situation.

You need to go into a meeting with the ability to widen your focus to take in the mood of the room and yet, on demand, narrow your focus to the individual slide you are presenting.

Solution-Oriented Approach

Developing a solution-oriented approach builds upon your ability to focus. Every day, you will face many challenges and distractions. Sustainable high performers know how to recognize distractions and how to choose to focus on developing effective solutions. There are plenty of people who thrive on the drama of being problem-oriented. A High Performance Mindset is knowing how to identify the opportunities that each problem presents and focusing on the solutions (rather than the problems).

Flexibility

On the surface, having flexibility may appear to be in direct conflict with having discipline. However, upon deeper examination, these two skills actually complement each other. Being flexible enough to step outside of your comfort zone while remaining disciplined enough to not get pulled off track is an extremely powerful skill. However, achieving this balance is only possible when you are confident, focused, and solution-oriented.

Action-Oriented Approach (Knowing to Doing)

Of course, in every High Performance Mindset there has to be adequate knowledge, but knowledge alone is never enough. In fact, when we were researching the development of Tignum, we found a book published in 1828 called Sure Methods to Improving Health and Prolonging Life. The chapters dealt with nutrition, sleep, exercise, fresh air, rest, and even positive attitude. When we did recent internet research, we found millions of sources on topics like performance, resilience, stress, fitness, performance, nutrition, and mindset. The problem is definitely not a lack of information. However, you need to be able to move from knowing to doing in order to capitalize upon your High Performance Mindset.

Your Personal Performance Mindset

Now that you have been introduced to the components that our clients commonly include, think about more of your own qualities, attributes, and skills that you would add to this list for a High Performance Mindset. Then consider:

How will you develop these qualities, attributes, and skills?

How much development or education have you gotten on the specific areas on your list?

Why do you think you did not learn about many of these components to develop a sustainable High Performance Mindset?

"I consider myself a high performer. I have an MBA from one of the premier international business schools, and I have probably received over 1,000 hours of leadership development in my 20-year career. Every decision I make potentially influences thousands of people at IBM. But in all of my education and training, I have never been taught how to energize myself, how to improve my focus, and how to personally prepare myself for a big meeting, negotiation, or presentation.

I realize that I've always prepared my slides, prepared my notes, prepared my calendar, but I left my personal performance to chance. I would usually make an agenda for my team meetings, but I wouldn't take even 10 seconds to think about my own intentions or goals. The idea of doing some mental imagery to create my state of mind and prepare my performance was completely unknown to me.

Now, that I know how to get energized, improve my confidence, and prepare my mind and body for a peak performance, I have moved from just being a good leader to being a true high performer. It's an incredible feeling to raise my own expectations and then to meet them."
Tignum Client

Benefits of a High Performance Mindset

So let's imagine that you acquired your High Performance Mindset, that you developed every one of the qualities or abilities that you defined.

How would this High Performance Mindset change your performance at work?

How would it change your performance away from work?

Consider these questions carefully, because this personal reflection is an important step to building your awareness and setting the stage for making real change. In addition, think about the outcome of transforming your Mindset. How would you recognize this High Performance Mindset? This question may seem odd, yet it is critical for lasting change.

If you lose 22 pounds (10 kilograms), you can see the physical results of this change. If you improve your push-ups, you can count the increase in the number that you complete. But since you can't actually see your Mindset grow and develop, how will you measure your success?

This is a vital question to contemplate because one highly intrinsic motivator of personal change is recognizing and appreciating the progress you have made. The only way to improve yourself is to practice, so it would be most beneficial for you to also take note of the benefits that you have attained in the process.

Following are a few measurements of success that our clients have shared with us:

People around you treat you differently. They acknowledge your contributions, they look to you for leadership, and they defer to you for answers to serious challenges.

You feel more energized. The things that used to drag you down and destroy your Mindset no longer have any impact.

You improve your communication with your co-workers, your spouse, your children, and your friends.

You get positive feedback from your boss, your co-workers, and your direct reports.

You are more productive, get more done, and therefore, are more successful.

Mental Performance Dictates Success

When we ask professional and elite amateur athletes what percentage of their performance is mental, they usually reply 90 to 95 %. When we ask top executives how much of their performance is mental, they usually respond with 70 to 90 %. This difference is interesting to note, since it is actually athletes who require a greater physical ability of strength, power, agility, speed, and sports skill.

So why do athletes rate the mental contribution for success so high?

At this high level of competition, they ALL possess the physical abilities needed to win; therefore they recognize that it is the muscle between their ears that actually dictates who will win. Similarly, when we begin working with our clients, many of them think of their Mindset as just a head full of knowledge. However, they quickly see how adding the qualities we listed previously can give them the edge they need to win.

The brain has 100 billion neurons with over one quadrillion synapses. This structure provides an amazing capacity to be trained. Although there certainly may be some genetic differences that contribute to a person's Mindset, every single person can improve on the qualities, attributes, and skills we have described.

Your mind is always learning and always practicing—so be careful what you practice.

The Tignum Performance Mindset System

At Tignum, we use three different levels when teaching and implementing Mindset strategies. Our approach first focuses on improving leaders' self-awareness to their own thoughts, self talk, and current state. We then teach mental imagery techniques to help our clients self-regulate their current state and to integrate the functioning of both their left and right brain. Finally, we help leaders build a sustainable High Performance Mindset by assisting them in the development of their own personal anchors and rituals.

The three levels of our Tignum Performance Mindset System include:

_Develop Your Awareness
_Improve Your Energy, Clarity, and Creativity
_Strengthen Your Sustainability

In each level, we help leaders design and incorporate the most effective strategies for their individual needs. Much research has been done on each of these areas, but the important thing is that you understand these concepts and how easily they can be implemented into your daily life to improve your High Performance Mindset.

How can you begin to create your High Performance Mindset?

Chapter Six
Create Your High Performance Mindset

Awareness, the first level of Mindset strategies, is a foundational component to personal growth, personal innovation, peak performance, and sustainability. Awareness of your Mindset is all about YOU. The more you get to know yourself (i.e., what makes you tick, your strengths, your beliefs, your passions, your stressors, your limits), the more energy you will have. When you combine energy with a Performance Mindset of clarity, creativity, confidence, and a positive outlook, you will achieve sustainable high performance in all areas of your life.

Your thoughts and self talk can be positive or negative. They can greatly enhance your performance or significantly destroy it. To help become more conscious of your thoughts and self talk, you need to catch nonproductive thoughts and talk before they do damage. You need to stay alert to three common self-talk traps: awfulizing, absolutes, and condemnation.

Dr. Betsy Shoenfelt, a sports psychologist, describes these traps in detail:

awfulizing – focusing on how bad or tragic a situation is and believing that you cannot tolerate the situation,

absolutes – thinking in terms of always or never, (that there are either total failures or a complete successes), and perceiving situations in extremes rather than in degrees, or

condemnation – focusing on the blame of others or yourself.

Negative thoughts and self talk will stop you from creating a High Performance Mindset, and they will most certainly affect your performance in adverse ways. Aside from making you ineffective, negative self talk will also lead to self-doubt and further poor performance.

Level 1 – Develop Your Awareness

By developing an awareness of your thoughts and self talk, personal feedback system, personal strengths, resilience, intentions, and your choices, you will no longer be a victim to your unconscious habits. Awareness of your Mindset enables you to set your intentions and to take advantage of the many positive choices that are available. Once you become aware of your thoughts, stories, and self talk, you can challenge them and quickly make them more accurate and productive. The faster you can catch negative thoughts, the sooner you can avoid the emotional cascade that naturally follows. This approach can greatly reduce the overall stress load on your entire body. In addition, the sooner you can generate productive thoughts, the sooner you can benefit from the positive emotions of achievement, love, and appreciation.

Tignum has gathered data from our clients on the workplace items that create the most nonproductive thoughts and negative self talk. The top four issues are meetings, e-mails, travel, and corporate change.

Meetings
"Oh great, another meeting. What a waste of time. How can I get anything done when I have to go to all of these meetings?"

E-mails
"I don't want to look in my in-box. I can't keep up. I bet the majority of these e-mails are a complete waste of my time."

Travel
"Traveling can be a real pain in the neck. It seems like I spend my entire life on the road."

Change
"Here we go with another change. I'm sure this will be like all the other changes, a big waste of time and energy. I've seen this suggestion before, and this is the same stuff we tried five years ago that didn't work."

*Make a list of some of the negative thoughts or self talk with which you struggle. If you can't
think of anything immediately, carry a notecard around for two days and jot down thoughts
as they pop up. You may be very surprised at what you discover when paying attention to
your self talk.*

R! Reframe, Reframe, Reframe

Reframing is a fundamental strategy for reducing the negative impact of nonproductive and low performance thoughts and self talk. It is also a valuable tool
for developing your sustainable High Performance Mindset.

Throughout your day, your inner dialogue is constantly running. The ability to
quickly stop nonproductive self talk and replace it with positive, high performance thinking is critical to improving and sustaining your Performance Mindset
and habits.

The following reframe questions can help you in any situation. The more you use
reframing, the more quickly you will develop your High Performance Mindset.

What is the dominant thought or self talk that you are struggling with?

Is this thought or self talk really true?

What is the benefit of keeping this thought?

How can you reframe this thought or self talk to be more high performance?

What is the benefit of doing this reframe?

What affirmation will help you rewire your brain to be more high
performance?

Can there actually be a benefit to a negative story or thought? Absolutely.

When people have the thought, "I can't believe how many e-mail messages I have—I'll never get to all of these," there is a hidden benefit. The benefit may be that they support their feelings of being overwhelmed and they give themselves permission to not feel like a failure if they can't get them all answered.

But what if they were to reframe this thought? They could reframe to: "I have a lot of e-mail messages, so I better get focused and prioritize them so that I can reply to the most important ones."

Which thought is more likely to lead to successfully getting the e-mail completed?

Which thought is more likely to lead to more stress and resistance?

Which thought is more likely to lead to a feeling of success and accomplishment?

What will be the impact of this reframe throughout the rest of the day?

You can try this exercise any time that you want a physical representation of how much negative self talk you are creating. Take 10 paper clips and put them in your front pocket. Every time you have negative self talk, take a paper clip from your front pocket and put it into your back pocket (or move the paper clips from right- to left-side pockets). Time yourself to see how long it takes to empty your front pocket. This is a very accurate reflection of your current self-talk habits. If you practice our Mindset strategies, you should see the time that it takes to empty your front pocket significantly increase. This is a great sign of progress.

Your Mind's Fabrication of Stories

It's Monday morning, only 30 minutes until the weekly planning meeting where everyone shares their progress on projects and assignments. You're sitting at your desk sipping your cup of coffee as you try to make a dent in your e-mail messages. Suddenly your attention is drawn to the conversation going on in your boss' office and her conversation on the phone.

"Yeah, things don't look good right now. This economy is really challenging. No, I totally understand. There's no other choice. This needs to be done. When should we deliver the news?"

You can hear her side of the conversation perfectly. Suddenly, numerous thoughts pop into your head: Who is she talking to? What is the choice? What needs to be done? Is someone getting fired? Are we losing another whole division? Is she going to drop the bomb on us at today's meeting?

Your mind is telling the story as if you were reading it aloud.

You walk into the meeting room and take your seat. You scan the room and think: Who could be the ones that may be getting the ax? Could I be one of them? Who hasn't made their numbers? Who hasn't been on the right side of the last couple of change initiatives?

Your mind is adding chapter two to your story.

Your boss comes in and sits down in her usual chair, clears her throat, and begins the meeting. Like usual, she goes around the table to hear each person's progress report. You can hardly focus on the presentations because your mind is so distracted.

When is she going to drop the bad news? Why does she keep glancing at me? As quickly as this question enters your mind you think: I must be the one who is going to get cut. Why else would she keep looking at me?

Your mind has concocted the worst possible outcome.

The meeting is almost done, and then your boss looks up from her notes and says that she almost forgot to tell you the recent news. She starts talking about the downturn in the economy and that the company is going to need to make some changes. Then she drops the bomb: "Unfortunately, the annual Holiday party is going to have to be cancelled."

She looks directly at you and says, "Joe, I'm hoping you can still put together the food drive, so we can do something nice for some needy families. This year they are going to need it more than ever."

Suddenly, you're speechless. Not because your boss' request was so daunting. You're speechless because the mismatch of what your boss just said and the story you had going on in your head just crashed at the intersection of what you thought was true and what was reality.

This story may sound silly, and most of the stories you constantly tell yourself would sound equally silly if you were to write them down. But these types of stories happen all the time. The human mind is always creating stories to try to relieve itself of possible surprises. It's a survival mechanism that at one time in our evolution was probably amazingly helpful, but now seems to lead us astray far more often than helping us to survive.

Where do these stories come from?

They come from the thoughts that your own mind generates. It has been estimated that the human mind has between 12,000 and 60,000 thoughts per day. With this many thoughts generated a day, and our innate drive to survive at all costs, it's no wonder that we fabricate so many stories in our minds.

Thoughts can arise from a belief or from an emotion. Sometimes you are overwhelmed by an emotion such as fear or anger. Suddenly, your mind supports that emotion with an array of thoughts, stories, and self talk. Other times, you have a thought (sometimes a habitual thought or story), and your body supports that thought with an emotion such as guilt, anger, sadness, or anxiety. While thoughts are in your head, emotions are what you feel throughout your body. Thoughts and emotions are intimately linked. Most emotions arise from four primary feelings: love, fear, joy, and anger. Often times, people are not aware of their thoughts and emotions, and therefore they have no control over them. Even worse, when you are unaware of these thoughts and emotions, you are being controlled by them.

The Magic of the High Performance Mindset

I have been thinking a lot lately about the magic key for improving Mindset. I have organized and summarized all of the coaching calls I've had with executives, the courtside conversations I've had with athletes, as well as the things I've struggled with in the fire service and in my personal life. If I had to categorize all these challenges with one word, it would be control.

It seems to me that the constant Mindset battle is really about trying to change things that we can't control. It could be the traffic, the late train, the delayed flight, the number of meetings or e-mails in a day, the demands and expectations of others, the needs of my spouse or kids, the price of fuel, the state of the economy, the political opinion of my friend, the cost of my children's education, the gusty wind on the tennis court, or the mountain of other challenges I face every day. The more I look at all of these things (that appear completely unrelated), the more I realize that they all share one common thread—I can't control them.

Facing this earth-shattering truth, I realize that I only have two choices: I can worry, complain, kick, scream, and suffer (a great way to move in the direction of burnout) OR I can laugh and focus on only those things that I can control (a great way to move in the direction of being a sustainable high performer). This doesn't mean I ignore all of those things I cannot control. On the contrary, if I ignore them, they will control me, festering in my subconscious and leaving me feeling inadequate and overwhelmed. The answer is to be very aware of those things I can't control AND to also accept that I can't control them.

Therefore, I need to work diligently to be aware of the situations in my life, be painfully honest with myself on what I can control and what I can't, and be passionately committed to action on the things that I can control. The key to making this fundamental yet monumental shift is to ask yourself: What can I control? What can I do? Then do it with an unmatched excellence.
Tignum Blog

Natural Talent Is a Myth

There is a popular assumption that most high performers are born this way. Geoff Colvin, author of Talent is Overrated: What Really Separates World-Class Performers From Everybody Else, proclaims that this conventional wisdom about natural talent is a myth. The real path to exceptional performance is a matter of choice, as he explains: "The best performers observe themselves closely. They are in effect able to step outside themselves, monitor what is happening in their own minds, and ask how it's going. Researchers call this metacognition —knowledge about your own knowledge, thinking about your own thinking. Top performers do this much more systematically than others do; it's an established part of their routine."

This ability to detach yourself from your own thoughts and to evaluate them objectively requires a high level of awareness, which can only come from extensive practice. Once this awareness is achieved, though, it provides you with an amazing ability to adapt to all kinds of changing conditions.

In the Fire Service, there is a perplexing commonality to most firefighter fatalities. In almost every case, the firefighters in the vicinity of the collapse or explosion (whatever killed the firefighter) had a gut feeling that something was about to happen. They didn't have extrasensory perception—their brains were taking in thousands of subconscious clues and something wasn't adding up. They were all simultaneously recognizing danger signs. Unfortunately, these firefighters and their company officers lacked the awareness of recognizing their own feelings and thoughts; and therefore they failed to act in a timely fashion.

Similarly, when business situations produce completely unexpected problems, you can pause mentally and observe your own gut feelings and reactions from the outside and purposefully ask these questions:

Why am I resisting this deal?

Where is my anger or frustration coming from?

Am I being hijacked by my emotions or are they trying to tell me something important?

Do I need a different strategy here? If so, what should it be?

Your Personal Review Process

In developing your awareness, you can also examine how you mentally review your own personal performances. After an important presentation, do you go back to your desk and review how you did? Or do you just go on with your day and forget about it? If you do review your performance, do you only focus on what didn't go well, what you did wrong? When you get into an argument with a co-worker, or your spouse, do you take a moment to reflect on what happened, how you reacted, what you were feeling? Or do you just go on possibly stewing over the argument or the outcome all day long?

The fact is that every interaction you have, every performance you have in your day is a learning opportunity. It's a metacognition opportunity to learn more about who you are, what you feel, and how you react. It is also an opportunity for you to see your diverse choices and develop new patterns, new solutions, and a new High Performance Mindset.

Tiger Woods has described how he reviews each and every round of golf. He reviews from a mechanical side, from a tactical side, and from a mental side. He goes over what went wrong but more importantly, he goes over what went right. The second part of this statement is what is most profound: Woods reviews each and every performance for what went right. Why would he do this?

When we work with clients, we ask how many of them consciously review their performances (meetings, presentations, reviews, negotiations) after they are done. Generally, about 50% of people raise their hands. When we ask the 50% who don't raise their hands why they don't review their performance, the answers vary. Sometimes they never thought of it. Sometimes they are too busy to take the time. Sometimes they get distracted. The point is that it is rarely out of laziness—it's just not a learned and applied strategy.

So what makes Tiger's process so effective? He reviews every round of golf for what went right. This means that he is mentally rehearsing (practicing) high performance over and over and over again. Woods began golfing when he was two years old. At age five, he broke 100 for the first time. Think about how many rounds of golf Tiger Woods has completed in his lifetime already. Imagine the impact on his metacognition, on his mechanics, on his tactics, and on his confidence level by rehearsing his own high performance over and over again.

Next, we ask our clients who consciously review their performances how many of them review the things they did well. Generally, two people or less respond affirmatively. Again, why is this? This self-performance review is not taught in business schools, not discussed in leadership development classes, and in many ways, goes against their natural instincts. They say, instead, that they tend to play every mistake they made over and over again.

In contrast to Tiger Woods, what are people practicing when they focus on their mistakes? They are mentally rehearsing their poor performance. So what will they get good at? You got it—poor performance! Does this mean you should ignore your mistakes? Absolutely not.

So how does Woods deal with his bad shots, his tactical errors, and his mental lapses during his round of golf? (By the way, every round of golf is full of these because perfection does not exist.) The key is to identify the error (awareness) and then to mentally correct it immediately. What would the shot have looked like and felt like if done correctly? Woods practices this over and over again.

The next day, when Woods is faced with the same hole, what is he more likely to do? Will he repeat his poor performance or his rehearsed high performance? The answer is evident by his successful record: Woods was selected as the 1997, 1999, 2000, 2001, 2002, 2003, 2005, 2006, and 2007 Player of the Year by the PGA TOUR (Jack Nicklaus Award), the PGA of America, and the Golf Writers Association of America.

Think back to one of your recent performances. It can be a work performance such as a presentation, a meeting, an employee review, or a negotiation. Or, it can be an away-from-work performance like a conversation with your spouse, an interaction with one of your children, or an interaction with a neighbor.

Write down five things that you did well. (Don't worry if this task is difficult at first. For many of our clients, this is new and uncharted territory.)

Now that you have your list of examples of high performance, read over it five times. How does this make you feel? Can you feel your self-confidence and positive feelings growing?

Now write down two things that you could have done better. These are generally much easier to remember. (This is a reflection of where you usually place your attention.)

Now rewrite these two things to have high performance outcomes. Write them as if you were watching yourself perform them perfectly. Add as much detail as possible. How do you feel while you are performing this way? How are people around you reacting? What are the outcomes?

Now read these high performance statements (rewritten experiences) 10 times. If you do the math, you just practiced high performance 45 times and low performance twice. Imagine if you did this every day, with multiple performances, at work and away from work.

Does this take a conscious effort? Absolutely.

Will it change your performance for the better? Absolutely.

Challenge the Status Quo

When you are unaware of your thoughts, you don't have a chance to consciously ask yourself, "Is this thought or story really true?" Can you imagine making a decision based upon half-facts or even fiction? Without a high level of awareness, honesty, and introspection, you actually end up making these kinds of ineffectual decisions over and over again.

Human beings are creatures of habit. We tend to stick with things which have worked in the past. The problem with this approach is that often we create stories in our minds that helped us survive when we were young, inexperienced, and ill-prepared to deal with the situation. This is especially common with children who grow up with physically abusive parents. However, the verbal abuse that comes from comments our parents, friends, teachers, and others have made also stick with us.

For example, comments like "you're so lazy" can lead to a compensatory pattern of never feeling like you can work hard enough or take a break. Comments like "eat this and you'll feel better" can lead to a pattern where certain foods are used as comfort foods to take away pain. Comments like "money is the root of all evil" can lead to an aversion of financial success where you always sabotage yourself just when you are reaching your goal.

When you're growing up and hearing these statements, you do whatever it takes to survive in the moment. The problem is that your survival mechanism often leads to keeping deep-rooted, distorted stories that continue to play in your mind, which then prevent you from achieving your potential. Becoming aware of these patterns, stories, and the thoughts they generate is crucial to developing new high performance patterns and to creating optimal health (mental and physical).

One Mindset pioneer, Byron Katie, aggressively challenges the stories that clients internalize that not only sabotage their success but also often destroy their health. In her work, the first question to be answered is: Is this true? This question is followed by: Do you absolutely know this to be true?

It is amazing to watch people's beliefs crumble under such simple questions, as they realize that what they tell themselves is rarely true. This isn't to say that people are liars. It's just that they have learned to accept an untruth to try to protect themselves or to create a false significance that in reality isn't effective or necessary.

What will you do to change your thoughts, self talk, and stories to develop a High Performance Mindset?

Following is a poignant Mindset story that one of our clients shared with us:

"When I worked with Tignum, I felt like I got a lot out of their strategies. Mostly, I focused on the benefits for my work and my productivity. As I improved my mindset, I was amazed at how much more effective I was. I had always struggled with negative thinking and I think changing my attitude at work was a huge step for me.

Away from work, however, it was a different story. For years, my husband and I were trying to have a baby. I went through test after test and I began to get pessimistic about my chances. One night, I was thinking about my day, what had gone well and what I would want to change. And, I suddenly became aware of the negative thoughts that I had about my chances for getting pregnant. Then it occurred to me that I could use the same paper-clip exercise that had been so helpful at work to help me change my thoughts about getting pregnant. At least, I figured it couldn't hurt to try it.

I became diligent so that every time I had a negative thought about getting pregnant, I moved a paper clip. Quickly, I learned that by reframing my negative thoughts, I could change my entire attitude. I started thinking positively about my own body, my likelihood to get pregnant, and my ability to be a great mother. I could tell that I felt different, but it seemed so silly to me that I didn't want to tell anyone. Nonetheless, I stuck to it and in the end, I changed my entire outlook.

This would have been good enough for me, because I had turned a stressful situation into something I could handle. But when I found out I was pregnant three months later, I was in utter disbelief.

During my work with Tignum, they talked about how our thoughts change our entire physiology, and I am living proof that it really does. I had given up on all other methods and interventions but when I changed my thoughts, I truly changed the physiology of my body. And, now I have a beautiful daughter to show as the results of this change!"

The outcome of this person's experience exemplifies that everything is influenced by your thoughts—your body, your health, your outlook, your actions, and most of all, your performance. Have you ever stepped outside and winced because it is raining? Suddenly your posture changes, you become tense, you lose a little bounce in your step. These physical things you can actually see and feel, but think about what is also happening on the inside your body. What impact did this have on your brain chemistry, your blood pressure, and your hormonal balance? The fact is that your thoughts definitely influence all of these things, big and small.

What impact are your thoughts having on your physiology?

Are your thoughts making you more healthy or sick?

Are your thoughts giving you energy or destroying your energy?

Are your thoughts making you a high performer or keeping you stuck in mediocrity?

How Hardy Are You?

Dr. Suzanne Kobasa is a leader in the field of hardiness (stress resistance). She developed the concept of hardiness at City College in New York after studying groups of people with highly stressful occupations. Her most famous research was done with AT&T, following over 500 executives during eight of their toughest years (in the battle of the deregulation of the phone industry). Dr. Kobasa found those who coped best with their job stress and continued to perform well, and stay healthy, had a certain hardiness which she defined by three specific characteristics: commitment, challenge, and control.

Commitment
Kobasa described commitment as being involved rather than alienated from aspects of one's life. People who find meaning in their work, their families, and their lives experience life as worthwhile and interesting. Viktor Frankl, a

psychotherapist who survived the Holocaust and the author of Man's Search for
Meaning, also observed that having a deep sense of meaning and purpose was
a key factor in surviving torture, starvation, and disease. Those who did not have
this commitment to life perished.

Challenge

Challenge is based on the belief that change is a constant in one's life. Successful
people tend to see change as an exciting challenge to embrace and master rather
than as a stressor to avoid. They welcome new opportunities to learn, grow, and
change when faced with challenges and do not perceive these opportunities as
threats.

Control

The feeling of control or ownership is at the root of almost every theory of effectiveness and motivation. People who are able to make critical decisions and to
make change happen have developed this sense of control. In fact, when you develop your discipline to focus your energy on those events that you have control
over rather than on situations beyond your control, you become more resistant
to stress and also more effective and fulfilled.

*By reflecting on the following questions, you can examine your approach (as well as your hardi-
ness) in life. For the majority of our clients, the initial answers tend to be shallow and without
much depth. The more honest you are, the more time you reflect on these questions, and the
deeper you dig, the better your answers will become. Building this awareness will help you improve your Mindset and your performance.*

*Commitment – What are you committed to? What is the purpose of your job? Why do you get up
every morning and go to work? What in your work makes you passionate? Where do you find
meaning in what you do?*

*Challenge – Do you see things as a problem or as a challenge? Do you resist change or do you
see it as a challenge? Where do you find challenge in your life? When you are challenged, do
you get excited or do you immediately feel overwhelmed?*

*Control – Do you spend energy worrying about others? Do you find it difficult to let others
handle their problems? How often do you worry about things that are out of your control?
What things are within your control?*

When we work with our clients, issues around commitment, challenge, and control constantly come up. However, when they create more positive ways to deal with these issues, our clients tell us that they can really feel the difference in their energy, outlook, ability to bounce back after setbacks, and their resistance to stress. At Tignum, we believe that developing your hardiness is the foundational step to building your overall resilience.

Capitalize on Your Personal Strengths

At Tignum, we also work with our clients to assist them in becoming aware of their individual strengths, their communication styles, the things that sabotage their success, and their approaches to solving problems. There are many different behavioral and psychological evaluations available, but our goal is to keep the process simple yet effective. The tool we use is the DISC assessment from Target Training International (TTI). This is an efficient tool for evaluation of behavioral preferences because it is quick and easy to take. According to our clients, it is also concise, accurate, meaningful, and easily applied to their Mindset, Nutrition, Movement, and Recovery strategies.

Whether you use a specific tool to determine your personal strengths, or whether you do some self-reflection, the important thing is that you learn as much about your strengths as you can. Knowing how to use your strengths to your advantage will set you up for success. As demonstrated by the tactics used by two infamous tennis players, a key to winning is to know your strengths and then to use them mercilessly against your opponent.

Ranked number one in the world for seven years and one of the most successful tennis players, Martina Navratilova was a brilliant serve and volleyer. It's not that her ground strokes were awful, but without coming to the net, she probably would have never won most of her 18 singles and 41 doubles Grand Slam titles. By knowing her strength and attacking the net every chance she got, Navratilova won more singles matches than anyone in tennis history. In contrast, her greatest rival, Chris Evert, recognized that her greatest strength was her amazingly consistent ground strokes from the back of the court. By using this strength,

Evert won more than half the tournaments she entered throughout her 20-year career and made at least the semifinals in 90% of all the events she entered. Two outstanding tennis players, two totally different strengths, two legendary successful careers.

In business, the same approach rings true. Marcus Buckingham, the bestselling author of numerous publications, including his latest book, The Truth About You: Your Secret to Success, has coined the "strengths revolution," after interviewing thousands of employees at every career stage. He believes that individuals need to focus on, develop, and use their strengths. When you do this you increase your confidence, you develop your talents, you become more passionate, and you enjoy your work more. According to Buckingham, this strengths revolution is "the key to finding the most effective route to personal success and the missing link to the efficiency, competency, and success for which many companies constantly strive." Everyone wins—you improve your creativity and innovation, and your company improves its chances for success.

The common thread of most leadership theories is to be the best you. This is why becoming aware of who you are, what your strengths are, what you like to do, and what you're good at is critical. There are great leaders who are introverted, quiet, and in some descriptions, even passive. On the surface, these traits seem to be contrary to the description of the proverbial "strong lead from the front leader." But these same leaders may also be great listeners who know how to bring out the best in everyone around them by encouraging them to step forward, take ownership, and rise to each occasion.

In contrast, there are also many great leaders who apply the famous Israeli Army line, "Follow me." They put themselves out there, they direct everyone and everything. They give moving speeches, set tough goals, and tirelessly push everyone to achieve them. These leaders have a completely different set of strengths and they, too, can be very successful.

The most important thing is to be authentic and effective. You can only do this by discovering and developing your strengths. Throughout this chapter, we have asked a number of awareness development questions that may have helped you better understand yourself, your strengths, your challenges, and your stories. Consider the following questions, and discover even more about yourself:

Are you introverted or extroverted?

When you're socializing with people, do you get energized or fatigued?

Do you need details or do you prefer focusing on the big picture?

In your lifetime, what was your favorite job or position?
What specifically did you like about it?

When you work on a team, what is the one role that you wish you would always get?

When you get your evaluation feedback, what is the one thing that your boss always compliments you on?

What are you really good at?

What are you really bad at?

If you could design your perfect job, what would it be? Why?

Chapter Seven
Expand and Sustain Your
High Performance Mindset

It is always amazing for us to see how much our clients naturally change their behaviors and performance levels simply by becoming more aware. They change so much during this initial awareness phase, yet often they don't give themselves credit for the progress they have made. Make sure to take a moment to reflect on the changes that you have already made. After working to improve your awareness of your thoughts, your performance reviews, your approach to change and challenges, your behavioral and personal strengths, and the stories you tell yourself, it's now time to take it to the next level.

In the Tignum Performance Mindset system, you will utilize your new knowledge and awareness to purposefully develop your Mindset of energy, clarity, and creativity. We use the word purposefully because this is an essential component. It is only through purposeful, habitual practice that you will cultivate and sustain a High Performance Mindset.

Level 2 – Improve Your Energy, Clarity, and Creativity

This second level works on the development of high performance patterns through research-proven mental visualization techniques. In this level, peak performance is not only possible but highly probable. When you combine the proper energy levels with the clarity of focus and the creativity of imagery, you will be amazed at the potential of your mind.

Every day, you use mental imagery whether you realize it or not. In your mind, you perceive things as going well or going badly. You fantasize about how you would like things to unfold or you awfulize your images to the ultimate doom that you expect to happen. The bottom line is that the brain (specifically, the right hemisphere) is designed to imagine a multitude of "what ifs." These images then alter your entire physiology, motor patterning, and ultimately your performance. Learning how to consciously develop the most high performance and healthy images is a huge step in improving your energy, resilience, capacity, performance, and sustainability.

"When the stakes are big, like they were in the following client presentation, there is no second chance for a first impression. In a world-class setting with top business executives, you can't miss the mark when you are trying to convince them that investing in your company is a win-win for all of you.

When I arrived, the first thing I did was ask my colleague to take me to the boardroom where we would be presenting. As I walked in I took in every detail. I considered: How big is the room? Where will I be standing? Where will the participants be sitting? How many participants will there be? Will they fill this room or will there be gaps? How will I make eye contact with them? How will I feel if I am connecting with them or missing the mark? Where will the screen be? Where will the flip charts and white boards be located so that I can make my points without turning my back to my audience? Where will my laptop be? How much space will there be for me to walk as I talk so that I can remain relaxed, energized, and engaging to everyone in the crowd? What will the temperature in the room be? What will the lighting in the room be like? Where will I sit when my team members are presenting? How will I transition myself into the presentation so it comes across as integrated and not disjointed?

Next, our team went to lunch, and we discussed the final details for our presentation. We considered: What types of questions do you think they will ask? Are there any people who may oppose our views? Are there any cultural differences that we should be sensitive to? Are there any personal stories within the group? We combed over our content until we knew there was no stone left unturned. We left feeling confident that we understood our client's needs and we could help meet them.

That night in my hotel room, I mentally rehearsed my presentation at least 100 times. I felt myself deliver our message, I felt my posture, I felt my voice as it resonated in my throat on each inflection, I felt the group's eyes locking on mine. I saw the slides, the room, the participants' faces and interest, my team members sitting on the side. I rehearsed every single detail over and over again in my mind.

I also practiced every 'what if' I could imagine. What if the person in the third seat is falling asleep? What if the person to my left in the second row tells me I'm full of crap? What if the person to my right in the first row doesn't seem to be following my English because I'm going too fast and it's her second language? What if the projector stops working or the videos lose their sound?

The next day, we delivered a fantastic presentation. To say that we blew them away is an understatement. This was the beginning of a multimillion-dollar relationship with this company. Even more importantly, it was the turning point in my career."
Tignum Client

Mental imagery is a skill that can be developed with purposeful practice. In order to use it successfully, you need to:

_understand the skill
_value the difference it can make in your Mindset and your performance
_put the time and energy into practicing it consistently
_create mental imagery visions/scripts that are multi-sensory, rich in details, and realistic, with high performance outcomes

There are numerous theories and speculations as to why and how mental imagery works. The intent of our discussion is not for you to become a psychologist, but to understand and to be able to use this powerful tool.

Imagine an old-time slide projector. (Before PowerPoint, we actually used slides for the major points we wanted to present.) Each click of the remote rotates the projector carousel around so the next slide drops in front of the light, and everyone in your audience sees the image. In your brain, every experience you have ever had (or imagined) can be perceived as a slide or an assortment of slides. This means that when you come upon a new situation, your brain quickly spins your slide carousel, searching for a slide that either matches or closely matches this experience.

Once you create these vivid images, and you play them over and over again in your mind, your body fires the same muscles as if you were actually doing the activity. This experience has been measured in the laboratory using electromyography with athletes. When athletes imagine themselves running a race, hitting a tennis volley, or shooting a game-winning jump shot, the actual muscles that they would use in these activities actually fire during their mental practice.

Mental Imagery for Business Success

Many leaders don't realize that their high performance has a huge physical element to it, as well. Their state (calm, cool, excited, or nervous), their posture, their voice, their eye contact, their mannerisms, their focus—all of these are physical actions similar to the actions used to kick a soccer ball.

Therefore, you can mentally create purposeful practice and actually improve your performance. This mental imagery is critical to developing a High Performance Mindset. In fact, our clients tell us that they sometimes use mental imagery throughout their work day. They may want to change their current state, such as moving from being solemn to more energized, or from cautious to more confident. Or, they use mental imagery to develop and improve their skills in listening, presentation, and negotiation, or in their tennis or golf games.

Another reason to use mental imagery is to improve upon past performances. This is similar to Tiger Woods' approach, where he reviews his past performance for things he may not have done well, but then he rips up that slide in his brain and replaces it with a high performance slide. Using this technique, you can use mental imagery to build new high performance patterns even if you just had a poor performance.

What if you had to deliver an employee performance appraisal to one of your direct reports who has a very abrasive communication style? And let's say that during your discussion, he verbally attacks your management style and implies that he should have gotten your job when you were promoted. In total reaction, you explode and let him know in no uncertain terms that he works for you and if he doesn't keep his mouth shut, you will get him fired.

Of course, everything that happened in this scenario could have been true, but it definitely wasn't a high performance experience. And, there certainly wasn't an outcome that will lead to a better performance tomorrow. After this meeting, you could have replayed the entire conversation focusing on what you did wrong.

But, instead, this time …

Envision yourself as calm, prepared, and confident. You are friendly and accepting but still very direct and accurate in your appraisal feedback. Instead of overreacting to his abrasive comments, you listen attentively to his comments, you acknowledge his competencies, you identify the things you agree with, and then you reiterate your specific expectations for him in the future.

In this way, by envisioning a positive experience, you have just created a slide in your brain that will more than likely create a high performance outcome in the future.

Identify and Visualize Must-Win Events

There are many must-win events that you may want to identify and prepare for in your day. Must-win events are those events that when handled with precision, focus, attention, and the proper emotions produce a win-win outcome. These can include the obvious ones like presentations, critical negotiations, meetings with the board, or job interviews. But there are also plenty of must-win (or high impact) events that often go unnoticed.

Prepare for the beginning of your day …
What are the benefits to walking into the office in a positive state of mind, energized, and ready to begin your day? You can do this by looking at your schedule for the day, taking note of its flow, acknowledging the must-win events of your day, and identifying your opportunities to recharge and regenerate. Then you can do a brief (two-to-three-minute) mental imagery practice envisioning yourself walking into the office, going through your day, and being in total control all day long.

Prepare for an important meeting ...

A great place to start before every meeting is to set the primary intentions for what you want to accomplish. Be careful not to focus on the most obvious ones such as closing the big deal, getting the million-dollar contract, or making everyone agree with your proposed actions. Think more meaningful, think long-term, think deeply. Intentions such as creating an atmosphere of trust, letting clients know that you care about their challenges and limitations, or letting your team know that you value their thoughts and opinions can pay huge dividends if you regularly achieve these outcomes.

By clearly setting your intentions, you can discover how easily your actions fall into line. Suddenly, you aren't reacting with a knee-jerk but you are actually responding and performing at high level. What types of details can you include in your mental imagery? Remember, the more details you include, the more vivid your images, the more benefits you will experience.

Prepare for the transition from work to home ...

If you put effort into preparing for work, doesn't it make sense to prepare for your arrival at home so you can have the positive attitude, focus, energy, and compassion that you want? How many times have you walked through the door, still on your cell phone doing business, while your spouse and children beg for your attention? What was the rest of your evening like? Where do you get the most satisfaction and love? In answering these questions, it seems to us that most people would also define many activities at home as high-impact events.

Prepare to go to sleep ...

As you will discover in the Recovery section, nothing is more important for your energy, regeneration, and brain performance than getting a good night of quality sleep. Why would you leave it to chance?

The practice of appreciation is a mental imagery technique that we teach our clients—a technique that has been extremely successful for reducing the time to fall asleep, quickly quieting a racing mind, and improving the subjective rating for quality of sleep. Instead of lying in bed and letting your mind obsess over all of the negative things that went wrong during your day, go backwards through your day and identify all the things that went well.

A Mental Imagery Exercise

Develop a clear purpose of what you want to achieve. What would be your best outcome? Set your intentions. Identify what feelings and emotions will be involved. Decide upon the perspective you will use to envision what you want. You may do well with an external perspective, as if you are watching yourself in a movie. Or you may do better with an internal perspective, as if you are seeing things unfold from your own eyes. Both of these techniques are effective so experiment with which perspective works best for you. Include as many rich, sensory-based experiences as possible. What will you see, feel, hear, taste, and smell? Develop the events in this imagery in a chronological way. Be sure you use positive and affirmative language to go with your imagery. Avoid negative phrases or words. Avoid soft language that implies this may happen. Develop your imagery as if this movie will happen.

After visualizing your specific experience, you can also write it as a mental imagery script. From there, you can record your own voice reading it so you can play it back when you need it. Or you can have someone else read it to you as you relax and listen. Or you can re-read your own script like you were reading a book and visualize the story coming alive as you read. The more you practice this conscious mental imagery exercise, the more natural it will become. Even the act of writing your script will make you familiar with the outcomes and images you are creating.

The more vivid you make your imagery, the more successful and potent the exercise will be. The more you exaggerate and emphasize what you will feel, see, hear, taste, and smell, the more powerful the visualization will be.

If you have difficulty accessing certain states on demand, you can start by remembering a time in your life when you felt the way you are trying to re-create. Then, tap into what you saw, felt, and heard. If you struggle to think of such a time, simply imagine it.

The more often you do this, the more easily you will be able to access any state you want. With enough practice, scripts will develop on the run, images will appear at will, and sustainable peak performance will become your norm. As an additional benefit, your body will be filled with hormones that produce positive effects, and you will become more healthy, energetic, and in control.

If you struggle with mastering mental imagery, you may have more luck using imagery from a disassociated perspective. In this method, you can imagine someone else, perhaps a mentor or an idol, performing exactly what you wish you could do. Once this image is clear and vivid, you can shift to an associated perspective. Simply picture yourself stepping into this person as if you were putting them on like your clothes. Now repeat this ideal performance seeing yourself as the peak performer.

"My secret is simple—practice. Whatever I practice, I get good at."
Tiger Woods

Level 3 – Strengthen Your Sustainability

Although the second level will create peak performances, this level offers the techniques and tools to sustain these performances. One element of being a swimmer instead of a floater is your commitment to consistent high performance habits, rather than leaving your performance to chance. Two great ways to firmly commit to your performance habits are to develop personal anchors and use rituals that will help you stay on track.

Mindset Under Pressure

I encountered one of the most powerful examples of Mindset I have ever seen on the NBC Today Show. Ann Curry was interviewing Ingrid Betancourt, the recently freed former Colombian presidential candidate who was captured in 2002 by FARC (Revolutionary Armed Forces of Colombia).

In the interview, Ann Curry was making the point that the usual response to this experience, after six years of captivity and torture, would be hate ... anger ... vengeance. As Curry was saying these words, Betancourt shook her head—saying "No, no, no."

Curry asked, "Why not vengeance?" Betancourt looked Curry in the eye and with calmness and compassion answered, "Because vengeance is a chain, and I don't want to be chained to that jungle anymore. When the helicopter left the ground, and I looked from the window, I thought I am not going to take any of this to my future life ... There is no room for hate or for revenge. I could have compassion for them."

Betancourt reiterated that she wanted to be free in the future; and hate, anger, and vengeance would only keep her a prisoner. This response struck me so deeply. The power of the thoughts and stories we choose to keep in our minds either frees us or imprisons us. Is making these choices easy? No, not at all! Yet, each Mindset choice we make will significantly impact our actions in life. High performance requires constant attention, reframing negative thoughts, and implementing positive habits. If Ingrid Betancourt can make the choice to eliminate negative and imprisoning thoughts that will control her mind and her future actions, then certainly we can eliminate the destructive thoughts and self talk that sabotage our success.

Today, when you are opening your 200 e-mails, standing in the security line at the airport, stuck in rush-hour traffic, or in your eighth meeting of the day, ask yourself if your thoughts are helping you to perform your best or holding you back.

Tignum Blog

Use Anchors as Shortcuts

Anchors are like shortcuts on your desktop that take you straight to the program that you want to access. By creating, practicing, and then using an anchor, you can quickly elicit the High Performance Mindset you want. An anchor can be a word, a phrase, or a visual cue. An example of a word anchor is the word "focus." As you practice your performance through mental imagery, you insert the word focus as your brain makes the connection to ignore distractions and create more conscious focus. Another great anchor is the word "breathe," which reminds you to take a deep, cleansing breath and to release your tension and relax.

"Confidence" is a word anchor used by one of our clients. Just before she goes in front of an audience to make her presentation, she takes a deep breath and says the word confidence. Quickly, her brain knows to improve her posture, to walk with confidence, to make eye contact, and to speak with authority. Of course, these are all behaviors she has mentally rehearsed and physically practiced, in association with her anchor. This way the brain knows exactly what her word anchor means.

An example of a phrase anchor is "let it happen" or "positive physical response." The meaning of these phrases may vary, but for the person using them, the meaning should be crystal clear. For example, one of our clients had a counterproductive habit of overreacting to bad news during negotiations. If a client's counteroffer was significantly different than his offer, he would visibly show disappointment or even disgust. This wasn't just a deal breaker; sometimes, it was a relationship breaker. However, by mentally and physically practicing his positive physical response, such as a soft nod of the head, a friendly smile, and inquisitive eye contact, he completely changed what had before been an unconscious negative response. Before every meeting with a client, he would anchor himself with the phrase positive physical response.

Many people use a visual anchor which can be a great way to also stimulate the right (creative) brain. One client was a huge fan of sailing. He kept a photo on his desk of the 12-meter sailboat that he and his wife enjoyed every chance they could. Every time he looked at this photo, it would remind him to not fight the winds of change, but rather to use the change to find new opportunities. This client, who had a reputation for being inflexible, quickly changed his habitual response and consequently, his Mindset. At one of our follow-up meetings, people on his team were commenting on his remarkable evolution and its impact on the entire team.

For some, an anchor may be a bracelet that reminds them to not sweat the small stuff or a bracelet like Lance Armstrong's that reminds him to "LIVE**STRONG**." Some clients use something as simple as a rubber band around their wrist, and when they need to refocus or increase their energy level, they snap it to reinforce their positive mental imagery.

It is important to remember that anchors do not, in themselves, create the change in your Mindset. The anchor is simply the reminder, the switch that completes the circuit. But first you need to build the circuit through awareness, mental visualization, and physical practice.

Create and Utilize Performance Rituals

Rituals are very important because they bring order and structure to chaos and change. We are creatures of habit, and it is our habits that make us sink, float, or swim. High performance rituals increase your personal control and provide comfort during unpredictable storms of stress. Rituals, however, only work when they are consistently implemented.

One of our clients shared that he would invariably be on his cell phone all the way home from work. He would walk into his house as he was finishing up his conversations. This would really infringe on his time with his wife and children, setting the stage for a rough transition from work. In order to encourage a more positive transition from work to home, he started stopping at a nearby park to finish his calls. Then, he would drive around the block one time to symbolize that he was no longer at work and he was 100 % at home with his family. This simple, small ritual changed his life. His attitude and attention changed so significantly towards his wife and children that this allowed him to not only develop his own focus but also to gain their support.

Another of our clients used to struggle with her Mindset when she initially got to work. She would feel overwhelmed with her to-do list and bombardment of e-mails, her assistant's reminders, and the pile of budget requests she had to sign. She felt like she was walking into a lion's den completely defenseless. Through coaching, we helped her develop a ritual where she would get off the Tube (London's metro rail) two stops before her office. She would walk the last three-quarters-of-a-mile and use this time as a warm-up. She would begin to visualize her office and what was waiting for her. She would see herself as completely relaxed and in control as she knocked off one task after another. This walk became a powerful ritual that helped her create the High Performance Mindset she wanted. Consequently, she also lost some weight, improved her fitness, and reduced her stress.

Rituals do take time and effort, but the benefits are significant. Most clients have told us that although initially it did take some real conscious effort, quickly the ritual became habitual and seemed almost effortless.

Evaluate Your Mindset Habits

Everyone has the potential to have a great Mindset. Some of us simply need more practice than others. You WILL get good at whatever you practice. The more you increase your awareness and practice the Mindset strategies we have presented, the better your performance will be. Sustainable high performance begins with becoming aware of your habits, your needs, and the benefits you want to attain. Too often people leave their Mindset to chance. Huge potential lies within reach if you are willing to shift from just knowing to doing.

Do you want to sink, float, or swim?

The choice is always yours.

You have Mindset habits that will make you **sink** if you:

_lead an unconscious life where you are unaware of your thoughts, self talk, and the stories you tell yourself
_are unaware of your strengths but very aware of your weaknesses
_are reactive to everything and respond to frustration with anger
_are unaware of what you are passionate about
_are pessimistic and immediately see change as negative
_constantly complain about things that are out of your control
_simply show up to meetings (no mental preparation or intention setting)
_dwell on your negative performances (what went wrong)
_do not prepare for home-to-work or work-to-home transitions
_do not use mental visualization to improve your performance
_do not have any high performance anchors
_do not have any high performance rituals
_are unaware of the impact of and do not use Mindset, Nutrition, Movement, and Recovery habits to improve your performance

You have Mindset habits to enable you to **float** if you:

_are aware of your thoughts, self talk, and stories but rarely try to
  reframe them
_are aware of your strengths but spend lots of energy thinking about
  your weaknesses
_have occasional losses of emotional control but see this as part
  of being passionate
_understand that change can be a great opportunity but still struggle with
  adopting this approach consistently
_occasionally focus on or complain about things that are out of your control
_prepare your content and presentation for your meetings and must-win
  events but not your Mindset
_review most of your performances but rarely make the effort to immediately
  reframe your mistakes so you won't make them again
_occasionally use Mindset strategies to transition from work to home or
  home to work, but not consistently
_occasionally use mental visualization to prepare for high-impact events
_have identified an anchor to help you with your Mindset but do not
  consistently use it
_do not have any consistent rituals to help you access your High
  Performance Mindset
_are aware of the qualities, attributes, and skills of a High Performance
  Mindset but rarely work on improving your Mindset
_are somewhat aware of the impact of but do not use Nutrition, Movement,
  and Recovery habits in an integrated manner to improve your Mindset

You have Mindset habits to **swim** if you:

_lead a highly evolved life where you are aware of your thoughts, self talk, and the stories you tell (high level of metacognition)

_consistently challenge your thoughts, self talk, and stories to see if they are accurate and high performance

_reframe any low performance thoughts, self talk, or stories

_are aware of your strengths and use them consistently

see change as an opportunity

_focus on the things within your control

_prepare content, presentation, and your Performance Mindset for your meetings and must-win events

_review your performances for what you did well and reframe what you didn't do well

_consistently use Mindset strategies to transition from work to home and home to work

_consistently mentally prepare for high-impact events by setting your intentions and using mental visualization

_use anchors to sustain your High Performance Mindset

_have consistent rituals that sustain your High Performance Mindset

_consistently work on improving your Mindset through an awareness of the qualities, attributes, and skills that you want to develop

_integrate Nutrition, Movement, and Recovery habits with your Mindset strategies to improve your Performance Mindset

Develop Your Performance Mindset Goals

The sustainable High Performance Mindset strategies presented in this section are designed to be integrated with our Performance Nutrition, Performance Movement, and Performance Recovery strategies. These Mindset strategies alone will not necessarily make you a high performer or increase the sustainability of your performance. In fact, it is very unlikely that you can have a High Performance Mindset if you are overtired, hypoglycemic, malnourished, or sedentary. The four Tignum pillars of sustainable high performance are intricately interwoven and dependent upon one another. The true power of personal innovation comes with the integration of Mindset, Nutrition, Movement, and Recovery habits.

In order to take everything you have learned and create a High Performance Mindset, you need to develop Mindset goals that are meaningful to you. To begin this process, consider the following questions:

What three action steps can you take now to help you improve your Mindset?

If you were to have a High Performance Mindset day, how will your thoughts and self talk be different?

How will you reframe your negative beliefs, thoughts, and self talk, specifically to review or prepare for your performances?

What is the anchor will you use to remind you of your High Performance Mindset and your sustainable high performance goals?

How will you implement Mindset strategies to increase your energy, resilience, brain performance, and capacity for sustainable high performance?

Section III
Fueling Up for The Big Swim

Performance Nutrition – purposefully choosing food (while not sacrificing the pleasure) to improve your energy, resilience, brain performance, and capacity in order to develop focus and clarity and produce sustainable success

Chapter Eight
What You Eat and Drink Fuels What You Do

Chapter Nine
Prepare Your Swimmer's Plate

Chapter Ten
Eating to keep swimming

Chapter Eight
What You Eat and Drink Fuels What You Do

"If I wear a pair of Armani underpants they do not become a part of me. If I eat a slice of ham, it becomes a part of me. That is why I worry more about ham than fashion."
Carlo Petrini, Founder of the Slow Food Movement

It's 2 pm and you're completing your final preparation for your client presentation at 2:30. You worked through your lunch break, making sure every slide is as close to perfect as you can make it. You double-checked your figures and spruced up your fonts. You did your final research to be sure to understand your client's needs. You've gone through the slides three times in order to be sure that you know what slide comes next, and which slide after that.

You run to the bathroom one last time. On the way out, you check your appearance and everything looks good, although you notice that you look a little tired. You realize that you are feeling a little flat, a bit low on energy. On the way back, it hits you that you never ate lunch. Your stomach is growling, and you're craving something sweet. With 15 minutes left, you still have time to hit the vending machine and grab a quick snack.

You get to the small kitchen area and luckily, there's still some coffee in the pot. You pour yourself a cup, and add some artificial creamer and two packets of sugar. You stir it, take a sip—not great, but it will do. You need something quick to eat so you scan the choices: milk chocolate bar, apple Danish, cinnamon roll, potato chips, pretzels. You choose the apple Danish.

You head back to your desk. It's 2:21, time to unplug your laptop and head into the presentation. You slam down your apple Danish, take a couple of swigs of coffee, and you're on the run. You head into the conference room, you quickly set up your laptop, and you're ready to go.

Or are you?

Nutrition is a topic of passion, a topic of pleasure, a topic of habit, and often a topic of frustration. Every single human being is a nutritionist at some level. Every human being needs food to sustain life and nourishment to support every bodily function. Unfortunately, nutrition is often marred with myth and misinformation. Nutrition is generally approached scientifically with little regard to the joy that comes with learning how to eat for fulfillment or for sustainable performance. We are here to change that approach!

Food is meant to be celebrated, and we don't want to take away from this tenet. Positive emotions actually enhance digestion, and so these feelings must be maximized. Our goal is to encourage you to make 80% of your choices to enhance your performance and health, and leave 20% of your food choices to indulgence and celebration. This approach (aka Tignum's 80–20 Guideline) allows the pleasure centers of the brain to be stimulated while reinforcing the positive self-esteem that comes with making overall healthy and high performance choices.

The relationship that you have with your food is a deeply personal one. It is a relationship that is formed by your family history, biochemical individuality, cultural beliefs, experiences with food, personal taste preferences, and the thoughts that you have when you think of food. The more aware you become of why you eat, when you eat, how much you eat, and the impact that your eating has on your energy level, immune system, brain functioning, and your performance, the better choices you will make.

"When I heard the word nutrition, I always thought of going on a diet. I thought of cutting out the stuff that I knew wasn't healthy. To me, nutrition was always about losing some weight, trying to reduce my cholesterol, and reducing my risk for heart disease, diabetes, and maybe even cancer.
One of the greatest lessons for me was discovering the connection between what I eat and how I feel. Even more important is the connection between what I eat and my performance in a meeting or in a presentation. This isn't something you learn in business school. It isn't something your boss tells you about in your performance review. It isn't something people talk about in a boardroom.

When you think of athletes, it makes total sense that they must eat in a high performance way. You hear them talk about pre-competition meals, post-competition recovery meals, even special snacks for during competition. When you watch the Tour de France, you see the riders actually eating during the race to keep their energy up and to remain competitive. Many days, my day is like the Tour de France—I'm running from meeting to meeting with few or no breaks.

When I learned to think differently about food, to think about the connection between what I was eating and the consequences on my upcoming performance, it really made a huge difference. Suddenly my brain fog was gone. No more falling asleep in meetings after lunch. No more mid-morning dips where I was starving, irritable, and unable to concentrate. Finally recognizing that food has a substantial impact on my performance has really given me the performance edge."

Tignum Client

Can What You Eat Really Impact Your Performance?

In 2004, British Celebrity Chef Jamie Oliver made a journey into the British school system to examine what was being served for lunch. Just like the US, Great Britain has been struggling with a growing childhood obesity problem. As Oliver learned more about what was being served, he attempted to revamp the school menu, while sticking to the smallest budget possible. For only 37 pence (approximately 54 US cents) per student, he created alternative menus that included healthy protein sources with lower saturated fats, vegetables, and fruits. His new menus also featured a drastic reduction in the traditional processed foods.

As expected, initially he ran into resistance from the food servers (most notably the head chef), and the children who knew more about McDonald's and Domino's Pizza than they knew about asparagus. But as the students started eating the new alternative meals, the results were startling. Within a month, the teachers noted a significant difference in students' attention spans, memory, overall behavior, and in their test scores. Similarly, the school nurse noticed a sharp reduction in the amount of medication she was administering and in the number of students coming to her office with asthma or other illnesses.

If school lunches have this great of an impact on these children, what impact do you think your food choices can have on you?

Back to the opening story ... This executive was so committed to delivering a high performance presentation that s/he even worked through lunch. Over 60 % of the executives who have worked with us state that skipping lunch is a common occurrence to ensure they get their work done. They also report that they frequently use coffee and high-sugar snacks to make it through their afternoons. Even more alarming, though, is that less than 5 % have responded that they have strategically selected their lunch to improve their afternoon performance. In this way, they are just like the students in the lunchroom—at the mercy of the school's established menu or vending machines.

Why We Need Food Vs. Why We Eat Food

Every function in the body requires energy. This energy comes from the foods you eat. Besides producing energy, food is critical in supplying the building blocks that make up every cell and organ in the body. Every second of life, the body is participating in thousands and thousands of chemical reactions. These reactions need catalysts to perform properly, and these catalysts come from vitamins, minerals, and trace elements supplied from your food.

Many people don't realize that their bodies are under continual renewal. In fact, every single day, your body replaces more than 300 billion cells. The integrity of this renewal determines how healthy you will be and how well you will age. The solution is to keep producing healthy cells, which can be accomplished by making better food choices— ultimately leading to healthy cell regeneration.

But remember, cell regeneration isn't just about health; it also impacts your performance. If you recall the presenteeism statistics, when your health suffers, so does your productivity and performance. Similarly, your body is an integrated unit so when one organ suffers, your body as a whole suffers, and this includes the functioning of your brain.

The food and lifestyle choices you make today will impact the cell renewal of every organ in your body in the future. This incredible opportunity to enhance cell renewal is why we encourage you to think differently about food. These choices will not only impact your performance today but also your sustainability for years to come.

Protein Improves Your Immunity

Protein is essential for more than the body's muscle mass. Its primary function is to nourish and regenerate the immune system, which contains cells that are made up of mostly protein. The quality of protein in your diet directly impacts the reproduction and functioning of these cells. Inadequate protein intake can impact the immune system's ability to fight illness and can also lower your resilience to daily stress, travel demands, and jet lag.

Properly balancing protein in meals and snacks throughout the day can steady your glucose levels and help boost your energy level and resilience, while also nourishing your immune system and improving your brain performance. Excellent sources of protein can be found in dairy foods (yogurt, cheese, cow's milk), eggs, meats, fish, poultry, beans, soy products, legumes, nuts, and seeds.

When you look at the various layers of your immune system—from your skin and the linings of your digestive tract (mucosal layer) all the way down to the production of white blood cells—you can understand why your body needs proper nutrition to protect itself. Your skin, the major barrier between the inside and the outside of the body, regenerates itself every two weeks. Therefore, good Nutrition habits are vital to ensuring that your immune system functions at its best.

The way you eat doesn't just affect the way you look. It impacts your energy level, your performance, your health, and your sustainability. With the proper Nutrition strategies, your brain performance and quality of time can be significantly improved.

Nutrition Impacts Your Brain Performance

At the Amen Clinic, our colleague Dr. Daniel Amen is using nutrition to help his patients improve their brain functions. Although a person's diet is rarely associated with ailments such as brain fog (loss of memory, slow to form thoughts, forgetting thoughts in the middle of sentences), anxiety, attention deficit disorder, depression, and dementia, Amen's research and clinical experience suggests something quite different. In fact, he is experiencing considerable success in using dietary changes and nutritional supplements to reduce these conditions where previously only medications were used.

In a study done by University Laboratory of Physiology at Oxford University, researchers studied over 1,000 young prisoners and the impact of fish oil supplements on their violent behavior. After one year, the group on the supplements reduced their violent behavior by approximately 33%. One researcher noted, "Our initial findings indicated that improving what people eat could lead them to behave more sociably as well as improving their health. This is not an area currently considered in standards of dietary adequacy. We are not saying nutrition is the only influence on behavior but we seem to have seriously underestimated its importance."

Imagine the huge economic savings if we could reduce violent behavior in our society by 33%. But the real lesson here isn't simply about violent behavior—it is about the link between nutrition and behavior. Imagine if you could increase attention span, improve creativity and self-control, and decrease brain fog by changing the nutritional choices you make.

At Tignum, we want you to think differently about the foods that you eat. Every choice you make is a choice that will impact your brain. High performance and sustainability are clearly linked to what you eat and drink.

Up to 40% of the way you feel right now is due to your last meal. The foods you eat directly impact the functioning of your brain.

Move From Awareness to Performance Nutrition

Awareness of what you eat, why you eat, when you eat, how much you eat, and the benefits you hope to feel after you eat is an essential component of the Tignum Performance Nutrition pillar. The more aware you become of your choices and the associated impact they have on your energy level, immune system, and overall performance, the easier it will be to change your nutritional habits. With a high level of metacognition or what drives your choices, especially the unconscious ones, you will develop control over your eating habits.

Increasing your awareness of your nutritional habits and motivations is a vital first step to developing personal strategies to move from eating to Performance Nutrition. Many people can't remember what they ate the day before. This may be because they don't really think about what they are eating, but rather they eat out of habit.

How many meals do you eat each day?

What are the most common reasons that you eat?

How do you determine your portion size?

Do you stop eating before you're full?

Do you always eat everything on your plate even if it makes you feel uncomfortably full?

Do you ever take note of how you feel 30 minutes after a meal?

Factors That Influence What Goes on Your Plate

Hunger

On the surface, hunger seems like it would be the most important factor in determining what foods you eat. However, studies have shown that people eat less than 25% of the time for true physiologic hunger, even though every innate mechanism in the body to regulate when and how much they eat is based upon this primal drive.

Social Habits

In the business world, attending business lunches and dinners is often part of the job. It makes sense that the pleasure of eating should be shared with the pleasure of getting together with business and social friends. Many executives complain that the frequency and food choices of these engagements make high performance eating very challenging. Frequently, business dinners begin with wine and bread. These choices alone can cause a rapid rise in blood glucose and subsequent food cravings and overeating. They can also leave you feeling lethargic and fighting to stay alert during and after dinner.

Time Constraints

Time constraints definitely impact your choices and the speed in which you eat. With more and more time constraints, many people not only seek convenience foods that require less time for preparation but they also consume foods faster. This goes against the body's normal gearing-up mechanism for eating, which produces the enzymes needed to digest the food that is coming.

In the US, studies have shown that many meals eaten are consumed within three to five minutes. Digestive enzymes are not fully activated until 20 minutes into a meal. Can you say indigestion?

Family and Culture

Food is part of the celebration of life, and every culture has some ritual and social structure around eating. Unfortunately, in many cultures, these social rituals can lead to obesity. In many families, food is equated with love. Parents demonstrate their love by feeding children their favorite foods, with little regard for calories or nutrients. As noted earlier, childhood obesity is a growing concern and top health issue in the US and the UK.

Stress

Stress has a big impact on why you eat as well as on what you eat. When your body is stressed, it responds with the fight-or-flight response. This response requires blood sugar for your brain and muscles to be ready for action. This is why when you're under high stress, your body craves high-sugar and high-fat food.

However, stress impacts everyone differently. Studies show that about 50 % of people eat more under stress while the other 50 % don't eat at all. Individual responses are dependent upon your physiological makeup and the blood flow to your digestive tract during stress. Neither of these responses (eating more or eating less) is high performance or sustainable.

Travel

Traveling can definitely impact the way you eat. A study in the US tracked people who travel and found that those who travel regularly consume up to 10 pounds (4.5 kilograms) more preservatives and chemicals, 10 to 15 pounds (4.5 to 7 kilograms) of extra sugar, and two times the trans fats that they eat at home.

Sleep

Sleep deprivation has a significant impact on the food choices you make. When the quality or quantity of sleep is not enough to meet your sleep needs, you will crave high-sugar, high-fat foods. This is because the brain knows it needs energy, and the quickest way for it to try to meet that need is to get sugar (even if it doesn't really need it). In addition, without adequate sleep, you may crave caffeine which can dehydrate your body and decrease brain performance even more.

The Benefits of Eating Slowly
Not too far back in the history of our species, gathering and preparing our food required a full day's work. Now the time it takes to whip up a meal or find a fast food substitute to eat is more like a sprint in our day.
When I did individual nutritional counseling, some of the most enlightening feedback I received from clients was that when they slowed down to really experience and appreciate their meals, they felt better! They also felt like they were sharper, more focused, and more apt to remember things.
I think there are many factors involved with this phenomenon of slow eating, feeling better, and performing better. One outcome of eating food slowly is that it positively impacts our digestion, since we are wired physiologically to release digestive enzymes at least 20 minutes after food is in the digestive tract. So by eating slowly, you help with the proper timing of these enzymes. This elevation of digestive enzymes leads to a greater assimilation of nutrients into the brain and the other vital organs. I suspect there are other factors—savoring the aroma of the meal, enjoying your time with companions, and appreciating the overall meal ambiance —that can also create authentic Recovery breaks. All of these, in conjunction with reducing the stress hormones which can be attributed to eating too quickly, can certainly lead to improved creativity, concentration, recall, and composure.
Tignum Blog

The Tignum Performance Nutrition System

We have developed our system to improve our clients' self-awareness of current eating habits (why they eat what they eat when they eat) and the impact that these eating habits have on their energy, resilience, capacity, performance, and sustainability. We teach strategies to assist our clients in self-regulating their nutritional choices to maintain steady blood glucose, improve the nutrient density of their foods, reduce the exposure of toxins to their immune systems, and optimize their sustainable performance and health.

The four levels of our Tignum Performance Nutrition System include:

_Hydrate for High Performance
_Balance Blood Glucose for Peak Performance
_Choose Nutrient Dense Foods to Enhance Performance
_Utilize Nutrition for Sustainability

In each level, we help leaders design and incorporate the most effective strategies for their individual needs. Much research has been done on each of these areas, but the important thing is that you understand these concepts and how easily they can be implemented into your daily life to improve your High Performance Nutrition habits.

Level 1 – Hydrate for High Performance

Water is a large component of the human body, making up 45 to 75 % of total body weight. On the average, the brain is made up of 80 % water, lean muscle tissue contains 75 % water, blood contains 95 % water, and bone has 22 % water. Thus, hydration is critical to mental and physical performance and your overall health. This level focuses on hydration strategies to build the foundation for all your nutritional habits.

Water is essential for all life. It helps your immune system, removes toxins and wastes from your body, assists in your digestion, improves your energy, and increases your mental and physical performance.

Conversely, dehydration weakens your immune system, negatively impacts your digestion, decreases the ability for fat cells to metabolize (making it harder to lose weight), negatively impacts your concentration, makes your heart work harder, and reduces the efficiency of your cardiovascular system. Dehydration also affects the transport of nutrients and oxygen, the ability to dissipate heat properly, and the ability of your muscular system to operate effectively.

Water is the principal chemical component of the human body. Every system in your body depends on water.

Normal brain function requires that brain cells are fully hydrated. Since the brain is 80% water, dehydration will lead to brain fog. Dehydration can decrease your attention and concentration by as much as 13% and reduce your short-term memory recall by 7%.

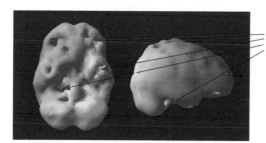

Areas of decreased activity due to dehydration.

Dehydrated Brain = Low Performance

Hydrated Brain = High Performance

Photographs provided by Dr. Daniel Amen from Amen Clinics, Inc.

How much water should you drink each day?

The exact amount is difficult to determine, since each individual's hydration needs are different. The amount of water you need is dependent on many factors, including your health, activity level, medications you take, your diet, and the altitude, weather, and humidity where you live.

Drinking a glass of water in the morning when you get up—to flush out the toxins your body has produced during the night—will give you a positive jump-start on the day. Drinking a glass of water with your meals, or drinking water **before** you get thirsty are other ways to prevent dehydration.

We encourage our clients to carry a one liter, non-BPA water bottle (without the toxic chemical bisphenol A in the plastic) with them to remind them to drink water consistently throughout the day. Drinking an adequate amount of water is not only important for brain performance, immune function, cardiovascular health, detoxification, and adrenal function; water can also help keep your stomach full and act as a natural appetite suppressant. Therefore, developing good hydration habits can also help you achieve and maintain a healthy weight.

It is important to recognize that not all fluids you drink will hydrate you. Certain liquids can actually dehydrate you. We call these drinks hydration-robbers and have categorized them into four types:

_alcohol (wine, beer, hard liquor)
_caffeine (coffee, tea, sodas, energy boosters)
_phosphates (fizzy drinks)
_high-sugar drinks (juices, sodas)

Note: people who consistently drink coffee or tea will adapt to the effects of caffeine and actually experience a reduced dehydrating effect.

Do you need to completely avoid these hydration-robbers? No, but you do need hydration strategies to compensate for drinking them. We recommend that you drink one to two glasses of water for every glass of hydration-robbers that you drink.

How will you know if you are fully hydrated?
The easiest way to measure your hydration is to monitor the quantity and color of your urine. According to the Mayo Clinic, "... if you drink enough fluid so that you rarely feel thirsty and produce 1.5 liters (6.3 cups) or more of colorless or slightly yellow urine a day, your fluid intake is probably adequate."

Executives have commonly shared with us that they have gone almost a full day at the office without urinating. This is definitely a sign of dehydration. In addition, dark or concentrated urine is a dependable sign of inadequate hydration.

US Government research recommends ingesting 0.25 liters (8.5 ounces) of fluid every hour that you're awake. This means a minimum of 4 liters (4.25 quarts) of water a day, depending on how much you perspire.

So, is water the only drink that we recommend?
Not necessarily. We understand that many times you may crave something with flavor or bubbles or a refreshment that can directly stimulate you. For this reason, we have compiled a short list of drinks that meet our performance criteria.

Performance drinks

sparkling water
Research evidence suggests that sparkling water can support digestion especially for those with indigestion or sluggish digestion. And, there is no evidence that sparkling water disrupts bone health or destroys teeth like soda drinks.

fresh-squeezed lemonade
Lemons are an excellent source of vitamin C, and the stringent nature of lemons has been used throughout history as natural support to the body's detoxification system.

vegetable juices

Fresh vegetable juices offer essential vitamins, minerals, and phytonutrients (plant-derived compounds associated with positive benefits) to support cellular function. Some good choices are beet root, carrot-ginger, and celery-cucumber-tomato blend.

green tea

High in polyphenol and flavonoids, green tea has been shown to improve immune and cognitive functioning and fight off free radicals. The recommended intake in current research is two to four cups of green tea every day.

coffee

Caffeine has been extensively researched for its performance-enhancing benefits, both physically and mentally. It has been shown to increase alertness and reduce fatigue, especially in low arousal situations (as in shift work at night). Additionally, caffeine in coffee has been shown to improve a person's performance on both simple and complex tasks.

What are free radicals?

Free radicals are a byproduct of metabolism within the body. They are formed when the molecular bonds are broken and an odd, unpaired electron is left over. Once a free radical is formed, it can be detrimental to the other cells so the body tries to quickly stabilize it. If these free radicals are not stabilized, they can contribute to cancer and heart disease. Antioxidants that you get from a high performance diet can help neutralize these free radicals by donating one of their electrons. Our Tignum Performance Nutrition strategies are designed to provide your body with an array of antioxidants to help fight off the free radical production from stress, toxins, and your own metabolism.

The Skinny on Coffee

There is so much misinformation out there about coffee. Contrary to some things you may read, coffee is not the worst drink for you. But that doesn't mean you can drink unlimited amounts. Research suggests that there may be individual differences in the way caffeine is metabolized. Some people can metabolize caffeine quickly while others may keep caffeine in their system longer (which is potentially more dangerous).

While much more research is needed in this area, it should be noted that most of these research studies were done with moderate doses of caffeine, defined as one to two cups per day. Similarly, in moderate doses, coffee provides healthy antioxidants that can protect you from dangerous free radicals. All of this is good news for those of you who love a steaming cup of coffee to refresh you and get ready for your day. (Keep in mind that some mugs can actually be the equivalent of three cups of coffee.)

In higher doses, however, caffeine in coffee may cause additional stress on your cardiovascular, digestive, and adrenal systems. It may also dehydrate your body and deplete important minerals and vitamins. The following client story highlights the positive effects of changing harmful coffee habits:

"Before working with Tignum, I was a coffee addict. I drank three or four cups to get going in the morning and another two or three after lunch to get ready for the afternoon. On some days, I drank another two cups around 4 pm just to make it to the end of the day. Not only was this an expensive habit, but I had always wondered if it was also dangerous.

After working with Tignum, I decided to change my coffee habits. It wasn't simply because so much coffee was bad for me. It was also because I didn't want to feel like I had a vice like this that I depended upon just to stay awake. When I implemented the Tignum strategies of drinking a full glass of water as soon as I woke up, doing 10 to 15 minutes of daily prep movements, and then drinking another full glass of water, my craving for morning coffee disappeared. I can't explain it but I felt more energized, and my desire for coffee just vanished. I also felt much better around 10 in the morning than I used to.

I still drink one cup of coffee after lunch but more because I love it. I find it relaxing, and it stimulates my digestion and gives me a little kick to start the afternoon. And, when I hydrate well throughout the afternoon I rarely, if ever, feel like I need a cup at 4 pm.

Now after six months of developing high performance hydration habits, I really feel much better. Especially since I don't feel like I have this vice anymore—I no longer need coffee to make it through the day. I never would have believed it, but hydration is critical to feeling and performing my absolute best."

The awareness question to consider is—why do you drink so much coffee? If you drink coffee to generate artificial energy to make it through your day, you may be in the danger zone. In this case, it is important to develop good Mindset, Nutrition, Movement, and Recovery habits and use coffee only when needed or for your enjoyment choices (Tignum's 80–20 Guideline).

During the day, what kinds of fluids do you drink that hydrate you?

What hydration-robbers do you drink?

How long do you take to eat your meals?

How does stress affect your appetite?

What types of foods do you crave or eat when you are stressed or overtired?

What kind of foods do you eat when you travel?

Chapter Nine
Prepare Your Swimmer's Plate

One of the most important strategies in high performance eating is to maintain a steady blood glucose level. When blood glucose fluctuates throughout the day, it affects a multitude of hormones and ultimately affects your energy level, mental acuity, memory, and even your immune system.

The best way to maintain steady blood glucose is to avoid skipping meals and to spread your daily calories throughout the day. By eating five smaller meals per day instead of two or three larger ones, you will supply your body and brain with the constant energy it needs to perform at its best.

Level 2 – Balance Blood Glucose for Peak Performance

Steady blood glucose is essential to a high performing brain. Our High Performance Nutrition strategies in this level are designed to eliminate spikes in your blood glucose and to give your body's cells a steady source of energy and nutrients.

When you eat large meals, your body responds by shifting blood away from the muscles and brain, and sending it into the stomach and intestines. It also raises your blood glucose, which can lead to a rebound hypoglycemia and a mental fog or energy dip. Avoiding blood glucose spikes and dips is critical for reducing brain fog, preventing energy slumps, stabilizing many hormones, and enhancing your immune system.

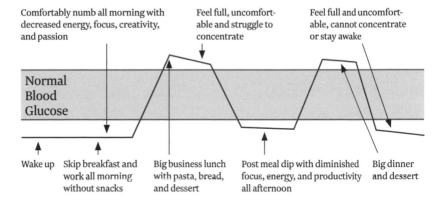

Spikes in Glucose = Low Performance

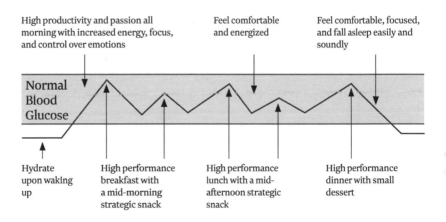

Steady Glucose = High Performance

At Tignum, we recommend a simple way to determine the proper portion sizes to prevent blood glucose spikes and to maximize steady energy levels. Even better, you carry the measuring instruments with you at all times—your hands.

protein = size of your palm (thickness and area)

starch (carbohydrate) = size of your closed fist

vegetables/fruit = size of an open hand (palm and fingers)

Professor Paul E. Gold, a faculty member in the Neuroscience Program and College of Medicine at the University of Illinois at Urbana-Champaign, has studied the impact of blood glucose levels on performance. He states, "Glucose enhances learning and memory not only in rats but also in many populations of humans. For schoolchildren, this implies that the contents and timing of meals may need to be coordinated with academic activities to have the most beneficial cognitive effects that enhance learning."

Given this research, low performance from unhealthy eating habits or poorly timed meals should come as no surprise. Since the brain cannot store any of its own energy, it depends on a steady source of glucose in the blood. Imagine the impact that coordinating children's meals and snacks (maximizing their learning) would have on their performance.

What does this mean for executives?

Simply put, the choices you make in terms of what you eat, when you eat, and how much you eat impact your memory, creativity, performance in meetings, and ultimately your productivity.

Studies have shown that executives under stress score higher on retention tests when they eat in a way that keeps their blood glucose steady.

Start With Breakfast

Research clearly shows that "breaking the fast" with a high performance meal is linked to improved focus and mental alertness, a decrease in mid-morning energy dips, enhanced resilience to stress, and more effective weight control. A high performance breakfast also supplies essential vitamins, minerals, and fatty acids necessary for cellular rejuvenation.

A high performance breakfast consists of three elements:

high-quality protein source such as eggs, cheese, yogurt, nuts or nut butter, lean meats, fish, chicken, soya, beans

source of complex, high-fiber carbohydrates such as whole grain breads, cereals, granola, fruits, and vegetables

source of essential fatty acids from oils found in olive oil, flaxseed, sesame, nuts, avocado, wheat germ, whole grains, and fish

Note: A blend of these essential fats is also found in eggs, soya, dairy, and some vegetables.

It is also important to note that skipping meals disrupts your body's metabolism and causes erratic fluctuations in blood glucose balance. These fluctuations can disrupt the way your body burns calories and slow the metabolism, leading to weight gain.

In addition, sleep studies reveal that one of the more common reasons for poor sleep quality is a drop in blood glucose. This drop is likely due to poor timing of meals or too much sugar or alcohol before bedtime. A small, high performance snack before bedtime can actually help you sleep more soundly.

Skipping meals contributes to food cravings and weight gain, poor concentration, mood swings, and poor sleep quality.

Strategic Snacks Boost Your Energy

Strategic snacks are critical for maintaining your energy level and also increasing your nutrient intake. When you are eating the correct (smaller) portions, you may find yourself experiencing a subtle hunger two to three hours after a meal. In order to keep your blood glucose steady, you need to have a strategic snack that has a blend of protein, some carbohydrates, moderate-to-low fat, and some fiber.

In the US, there is a comprehensive market of nutritional bars to meet this need. Unfortunately, choosing a high performance snack bar can be a bit tricky, since some are more like candy bars than real food. Historically, the original performance bars were designed and developed to quickly provide glucose (sugar) to exercising muscles. Today, these bars have evolved to provide nutritional supplementation, and in some cases, they can be used as a meal replacement.

However, if you choose a nutritional bar or any snack that is too high in sugar, too low in fiber, or too low in adequate protein or unsaturated fats, there is a high likelihood that you will find yourself feeling sluggish and tired, as well as experiencing brain fog. This is the opposite of the high performance state that we want you to develop.

Make the Best Nutritional Choices

There are lots of different health bars, but just because a bar has the word "health" on it doesn't make it a high performance bar. The best choice is to select real food, but with your busy schedules, travel demands, and the unavailability of refrigeration, we recognize that this choice is not always possible. In these cases, we recommend that you use the following factors to choose the best bar or snack:

carbohydrate-to-protein ratio
Try to keep a ratio as close to 2 grams of carbohydrate for every 1 gram of protein. For example, if there are 22 grams of carbohydrate, there should be approximately 11 grams of protein.

fat
Look for a bar that contains 5 to 10 grams of fat. Preferably the majority of this fat should be monounsaturated. Be sure there are no trans fatty acids such as hydrogenated fats or partially hydrogenated oils.

fiber
Aim for 3 to 5 grams of fiber. Fiber is very important for digestive system function and for maintaining steady blood glucose.

sugar-to-carbohydrate ratio
Try to keep the ratio of sugar to total carbohydrate to no more than 1 to 2. For example, if there are 22 grams of carbohydrates in a snack or bar, there should be no more than 11 grams of sugar.

portion size
A snack or bar should ideally provide 200 to 280 calories of energy. This is adequate to support high performance brain functioning while stimulating metabolism and not leading to unhealthy weight gain.

In addition to high performance bars, we recommend the following choices for high performance snacks:

_a piece of fruit with nuts
_yogurt with fruit
_cottage cheese with fruit
_cheese with whole wheat crackers
_hardboiled eggs and whole grain or sprouted bread
_trail mix with dried fruit
_hummus with whole grain crackers and red pepper or carrot strips
_a small cup of soup with whole grain roll
_peanut butter with a banana or apple
_half of a turkey and Swiss cheese sandwich

Power Your Brain by Going Nuts

Our clients are often looking for a high power snack to stabilize their blood glucose and to improve their brain performance. Research suggests that nuts and seeds may boost cognitive performance, stabilize moods, and support steady blood glucose levels, which will ultimately maintain sustainable energy.

Nuts and seeds are rich in essential fatty acids known as omega-3 fatty acids, a major component of brain tissue and important for both mood stabilization and brain performance. Omega-3 fatty acids support adequate levels of the brain hormone serotonin, which helps control both mood and appetite, thus playing a role in weight control, emotional well-being, and the reduction of mental fatigue.

B vitamins and micronutrients such as selenium, magnesium, and chromium—also found in nuts and seeds—have been linked to optimizing overall cognitive function such as memory retrieval, alertness, and mental stamina.

In addition, nuts (especially almonds and walnuts) have been shown to play a part in protecting brain cells from oxidative damage and supporting a healthy aging process and brain cell functioning.

The next time you need an easy, all natural, brain-boosting snack, I recommend you just
Go Nuts …
Tignum Blog

Plan for High Performance

One of the best strategies to have control over your food choices is to bring a portable food bag. This may be a change in your Mindset, but it will prevent you from being at the mercy of others. You can bring your own snacks to meetings or keep snacks in your office. Examples of good snacks include individual protein shake packets (just add water or juice), nuts or seeds, dry cereals with dried fruits, energy bars, cheese, hummus, yogurt, and hardboiled eggs.

How many times have you been to a restaurant, looked at the menu, and wondered what was the best choice for high performance?

Restaurants often serve about 25-40 % larger portions than what you need and use more saturated fats than home-cooked meals. The key to restaurant eating is to fill up without filling out. If you are a business person who travels and has to eat out, understanding how to make good choices can significantly impact your energy levels, your performance, and your health.

Dos and Don'ts to Maintain Steady Blood Glucose

Do
_have small regular meals
_have strategic snacks (nuts, seeds, hummus, energy bars)
_eat complex carbohydrates (whole grains, fruits, vegetables)
_eat food rich in B vitamins (whole grains, beans, nuts, fish, poultry, bananas, avocados, green leafy vegetables)
_eat foods rich in chromium (whole grains, mushrooms, beets, grapes/raisins, broccoli)
_combine protein foods with complex carbohydrates
_limit caffeinated and high-sugar drinks
_limit alcoholic drinks

Don't
_skip meals
_eat oversized portions or large meals that overfill you
_eat refined carbohydrates (white flours, cakes, biscuits, sweets, hidden sugar in foods)
_eat mostly processed foods
_drink mostly caffeinated or high-sugar drinks
_drink alcohol in excess

Level 3 – Choose Nutrient Dense Foods to Enhance Performance

Every food can be evaluated by the number of nutrients it has in relation to the number of calories it contains. Studies have shown that a nutrient dense diet has a positive impact on performance, health, and weight control. Our High Performance Nutrition strategies in this level are designed to maximize every calorie you eat by choosing nutrient dense foods and avoiding empty calories (with little nutrient concentration).

Traditionally, the American diet has been famous for producing overfed yet malnourished people. Unfortunately, this trend has spread to the UK and many of the other European Union countries. The reason is simple: In a society where so many people eat fast food, highly processed foods, and foods that aren't taken straight from the earth, the chances of eating lots of calories with few nutrients is very high. On the surface, this may seem like a bad trend only in terms of weight gain and obesity. Unfortunately, the impact on brain fog, energy levels, performance, sustainability, and health is also deleterious.

Statistics show that by simply adding fresh fruits and vegetables to two out of three meals or snacks eaten in a day, the nutrient intake for your day can be increased by 35 to 42 %. This is a significant improvement in getting essential nutrients.

What are these nutrients? They are vitamins, minerals, and other phytonutrients. Although they don't provide energy themselves, they are critical in the reactions that release energy from carbohydrates, proteins, and fats. They also support every single bodily function and are essential for high performance, immune function, and cellular regeneration.

With eating comes choice. For some, it's a choice of which fast food establishment to go to. For others, it's a choice at a vending machine. For others, it may be a choice of which entrees to order off the menu. For others, it's a choice of what food to prepare at home. In today's society, there are a multitude of choices.

Nutrient Dense Foods

garlic, leafy green vegetables, salmon, olive oil, ginger, beans, kiwi, berries, apricot, mango, papaya, bok choy, squash, kale, sweet potato, beet roots, and quinoa (high-protein whole grain grown in South America)

Dr. Joel Fuhrman, a US family physician and one of the leading experts on nutrition and natural healing, has proven that eating a nutrient dense diet is the key to optimal health, high performance, and weight control. Through his research and hundreds of nutritional science studies, Fuhrman has found that life span is lengthened significantly when subjects eat a high nutrient diet. He has developed the following equation for eating to live:

Health = Nutrients / Calories

Using this equation is simple. To achieve good health, you need to eat foods with high nutrients and low calories. If you eat a diet that is mostly composed of live foods (such as fresh vegetables and fruits), you will improve the nutrient density of your diet and ultimately your performance and health. Dark green vegetables are the best choice, since they have the most nutrients of all.

The Color of High Performance Foods

In order to help our clients think differently about the food choices they make, our Director of Nutrition Patti Milligan developed the Tignum Color Code of Restorative Nutrition. This diagram evolved from a meta-analysis of numerous studies and reports on food pigmentation and its impact on physiological function. The color codes were created to help simplify the importance of eating a variety of foods on a regular basis.

So often, people underestimate the impact of the choices they make. The Tignum Color Code Body shows the profound impact that various pigmented fruits and vegetables have on the many systems in your body. By increasing your awareness of the benefits of the choices you make in selecting your foods, you can improve your energy, resilience, brain performance, and health, as well as increasing your capacity, sustainability, and overall performance.

We have provided some examples of food choices below, using the system outlined in our Tignum Color Code Body.

Yellow foods optimize your brain functions:

_yellow squash
_corn
_yellow peppers
_pineapple

Red foods support your heart and circulatory systems:

_strawberries
_red peppers
_cranberries
_beets

Green foods rejuvenate your muscles and bones:

_spinach
_kale
_broccoli
_squash
_green leafy vegetables

White foods enhance your immune and lymphatic systems, and improve your cellular recovery:

_onion
_garlic
_ginger
_cauliflower

Orange foods support your skin and digestive tract:

_papaya
_mango
_sweet potato
_carrots

Purple foods promote your microcirculation:

_eggplant
_prunes
_plums
_blueberries
_blackberries

"We are often taught to eat a rainbow, in terms of the colors of our food choices. I could easily recite this directive, but it didn't have any meaning to me. When I saw the color code body for the first time, I had an aha moment. When I actually saw the benefits of eating different color foods, it made perfect sense.

Now, whether I'm preparing my own meals or eating out in restaurants, I find myself looking for a variety of colored foods. This approach not only improves the amount of nutrients I eat, but it also reduces the amount of processed foods I consume. Since I travel a lot, it is also a great way to eat high performance foods, regardless of which country I am in. The foods may change, but my drive to get the color of foods I need doesn't.

Making this simple change in my diet resulted in a weight loss of nine pounds (four kilograms) in my first month after working with Tignum. And, eating more colored foods has made me feel better and definitely more energetic."
Tignum Client

The following illustration exemplifies two different days with two different sets of performance outcomes. On the low nutrient density day, you can see that the foods eaten are very high in calories, very low in nutrients, high in saturated fats, and high in sugar. The impact on your performance from this type of eating will be significant. You will be lethargic and sleepy, and you may experience mood swings and brain fog. These food choices will negatively impact your performance in any must-win events that you have on your schedule.

On the high nutrient density day, you can see that the caloric load is lower, the amount of nutrients is much higher, and the foods eaten are high in fiber and high in healthy (monounsaturated) fats. The impact on your performance from this type of eating will also be significant, but directly opposite of the previous example. You will have improved energy, better cognitive functioning, increased concentration, and enhanced mental clarity. These kinds of food choices will also have a positive impact on your heart, blood vessels, brain, and ultimately, your health. You will be ready and able to effectively deal with any meeting, negotiation, or must-win event of your day.

	LOW Nutrient Density	**HIGH Nutrient Density**
Breakfast	pastry and coffee with cream	oatmeal and berries with green tea and cranberry juice
Lunch	hamburger, french fries, and soda	turkey breast sandwich with lettuce/tomato on whole grain bread and iced tea
Dinner	white pasta with marinara sauce, iceberg lettuce salad, garlic bread or roll, and soda	grilled salmon, Caesar salad, broccoli, brown rice, and red wine or sparkling water
Snack 1	bag of chips and soda	banana with peanut butter
Snack 2	muffin or candy bar	handful of nuts (walnuts or almonds)
TOTAL Calories	3,800 calories	2,400 calories
TOTAL Nutrients	minimal phytonutrients	> 64 phytonutrients
Vitamins	minimal vitamins	lots of vitamins
Fats	high trans fatty acids and saturated fats	high in monounsaturated fats
Fiber/Sugar	high in sugar and low in fiber	high in fiber and low in sugar

Use Food Labels to Make Better Choices

Learning to read food labels is another way to increase your awareness about what you are eating and to make better choices. However, keep in mind that each country's governing body has its own laws regarding what goes on the label.

Most importantly, if you are reviewing a label on a food product, generally it means that it is not fresh food. Therefore, it already falls into a category with some degree of processing. You need to weigh how much or how often you want to use processed foods. It is always better to choose fresh foods when you have this option and the time to prepare them.

Tignum Guidelines

Choose foods with a 4 to 1 carbohydrate-to-protein ratio.
Labels usually list the amount of macronutrients (protein, carbohydrates, fats) that are contributing to the calories of the product. Look at the ratio of these nutrients in order to pick a food that will help steady your blood sugar. Try to choose an item that has no more than a 4-to-1 ratio of carbohydrate to protein. This is critical for keeping your blood glucose steady. For example, if you are examining a label that has 35 grams of carbohydrate, then it should have at least 9 grams of protein or more. (Note: This is a higher ratio than our recommendation for high performance snacks because you will be getting the majority of your protein from foods without labels.)

Choose foods with healthy fats.
Review the type of fats. You should reduce or eliminate all hydrogenated trans fats and partially hydrogenated fats. Additionally, most of your fats should be monounsaturated. The higher the percentage of the total fats that are unsaturated, the better the choice.

Choose foods that are lower in carbohydrates and sugar.
Review the total amount and type of carbohydrates. With a high performance food choice, the sugar grams should be less than half of the total carbohydrate grams. For example, if the carbohydrate level is 34 grams, there should be no more than 17 grams of sugar.

Choose foods with fewer preservatives and chemicals.
Review the list of ingredients and see how many you can pronounce. When a product contains chemical preservatives, food colorings, dyes, and artificial ingredients, the words are usually unfamiliar, unless you have an extensive chemistry background. If you can't pronounce it, then you probably don't need or want it.

To download the Tignum Color Code Body, go to www.tignum.com/sinkfloatswim. Log in with the password "swimmer" to access our High Performance Nutrition information.

Now that you know some High Performance Nutrition strategies, consider the following:

What are some high performance snacks that you can keep at the office to maintain your blood glucose level throughout the day?

What specific foods (or colors of foods) do you need to eat more of?

What different kinds of choices can you make during your day to eat in a high performance way?

What are some high performance foods that you can eat with a busy schedule or while you travel?

Chapter Ten
Eating to keep swimming

Once you have increased your nutritional awareness and changed your eating habits to stay hydrated, keep your blood glucose steady, and increase your nutrients, you will be well on your way to becoming a sustainable high performer.

In order to maintain sustainable high performance, you need to address the toxins that are found in a diet containing processed foods and artificial ingredients. Although your body naturally detoxifies itself daily, eating certain foods and avoiding other foods can support and further this detoxification. In addition, due to highly demanding lives, it may be difficult to get all of the nutrients you need in your daily diet. Sometimes, supplementation may be warranted and beneficial.

Level 4 – Utilize Nutrition for Sustainability

This level of our Tignum Performance Nutrition System will take you even further, promoting opportunities to detoxify your body, to use supplements to eliminate any deficits you may have in your diet, and to develop individual strategies. You will also learn to use specific Nutrition strategies to effectively deal with business luncheons or dinners, busy travel schedules, and must-win or high-impact events.

Your body is naturally and constantly detoxifying itself. Even when you are unaware that it's happening, your body is working to maintain its balance and to create an optimal internal environment for its functions. There are five systems involved with detoxification and the elimination of waste products from the body. These include the respiratory, gastrointestinal (GI), urinary, skin, and lymphatic systems. When all of these systems are functioning properly, detoxification happens naturally and effectively.

Over time, however, toxins can accumulate and your body's capability to detoxify may be reduced. With toxins coming from so many sources, people are being exposed to higher quantities and strengths of environmental toxins. These toxins include pollutants, pesticides, chemicals, electromagnetic fields, and radiation. Additionally, there are toxins in your food from preservatives, chemical additives, artificial colorings, artificial sweeteners, and hormones.

The Benefits of Detoxification

For thousands of years, eastern philosophies have taught the value of seasonal detoxification (detox) rituals. More recently, western researchers looking to understand the underlying causes of certain diseases are finding that there are links between disease and the body's inability to clear out toxins. As these toxins accumulate, they increase the risk of heart disease, cancer, irritable bowel syndrome, emotional stress, joint pain, and anxiety. This can lead to a systemic inflammation and negatively impact the communication among cells. Since the body is an integrated unit, this can also lead to a lack of energy and the onset of disease, chronic body pain, and decreased performance.

How can you reduce the amount of toxins you take in through your diet?

How can you reduce the toxins from your environment?

There are many different approaches and methods to detoxifying your body; however, most of these are outside the scope of this book. We recommend that before you participate in any advanced detox program that you contact your doctor or another qualified health professional.

If you have implemented the first three levels of strategies from the Tignum Performance Nutrition System, you are already doing a mild and natural detox. The following foods and drinks will also contribute to your body's detoxification:

_deep green vegetables
_unsweetened cranberry juice
_ginger
_green tea

Use Supplements for Sustainability

In theory, you should be able to get all of your nutrient needs met through your diet. Unfortunately, with our current farming and transportation practices, you would need to eat in excess of 5,000 to 6,000 calories a day just to meet your optimal restorative health requirements. At this rate, most people would become obese. This is why we advocate eating nutrient dense foods and avoiding empty calorie foods (with high sugar/low nutrients) as much as possible.

It is also important to recognize that there is no one diet that fits everyone. In fact, Ayurveda, the science of life, prevention, and longevity—considered the oldest and most holistic medical system practiced in India—has addressed this individuality for 5,000 years. The Ayurvedic diet takes into account a person's age, gender, and constitution (dosha), as well as the season.

Similarly, Roger J. Williams, PhD, author of Biochemical Individuality: Key to Understanding What Shapes Your Health, confirms that we are all different, and this diversity is critical to the survival of our species. These differences create variations in your ability to digest and assimilate foods (enzymatic make-up), your endocrine response to foods, and your body's ability to excrete foods. Ultimately, this variation in your body chemistry creates your unique nutritional needs.

Dr. William Wolcott, author of The Metabolic Typing Diet, also feels that the rising obesity rates, the prevalence of cancer and heart disease, as well as many other diet-related diseases are partially due to our metabolic individuality. He states that our individuality creates serious dietary deficiencies when we try to eat in a one-size-fits-all manner.

So, why is this individuality important?

It's important because when it comes to taking nutritional supplements, what's good for one person isn't always good for another. Therefore, the only way to truly utilize supplements in a beneficial and high performance way is to work with a qualified health practitioner who thoroughly understands your needs. With that said, generally speaking there are a few nutritional supplements that may benefit certain people.

General recommendations:
_Busy people who are under high stress should take a multivitamin/mineral.
_Most women should take iron (for anemia due to menstruation), as well as calcium/magnesium and boron (for bone health), and folic acid (to support red blood cells).
_Soda drinkers and those who eat high-sugar diets need selenium, magnesium, and B vitamins (for metabolism and to replace water-soluble vitamins excreted in urine).
_Smokers should consider taking Vitamin C (an antioxidant), and zinc (an immune system booster).
_People who exercise intensely and regularly should take an antioxidant cocktail that includes beta carotene, Vitamin C, Vitamin E, and selenium (to combat free radicals created during exercise).
_Finally, new research suggests that people who spend more than 80% of their time indoors (unfortunately, this is becoming more common) will also benefit from a multivitamin/mineral that contains adequate Vitamin D (for calcium absorption and bone modeling).

Business Dinner Strategies

Business dinners often provide opportunities to develop relationships and accomplish important business negotiations. But these things can happen only if you are fully awake, perceptive, creative, energetic, and focused.

The following tips are designed to ensure you are at your best for the entire dinner meeting:

Remember that your business dinner actually begins at breakfast. Eating a good breakfast and lunch, and having small strategic snacks throughout the day will tame your appetite, give you energy, and prevent binging at dinner.

Eat a small balanced snack (with protein and some fat) before arriving at your business dinner. This will prevent your blood glucose from falling and keep your brain alert during the socializing time before dinner arrives. A small snack also helps absorb alcohol and prevents you from getting sleepy.

Make water your primary drink throughout dinner. This will help you stay hydrated, reduce the amount of alcohol you drink, avoid overeacting, and improve your digestion.

Strategically select foods that stabilize your blood glucose. Foods like nuts, cheese, beans, and meat will stabilize your blood glucose, while breads and pastries will cause your blood glucose to spike and then crash.

If you are going to eat dessert, you may want to trade some of your carbohydrates from your appetizer and your meal. Instead of choosing bread, pasta, rice, or potatoes to go with your meal, select a delicious dessert. This will help you stay within the Tignum 80 – 20 Guideline and get enjoyment from your meal.

Watch your portion size. Many restaurants serve meals that could actually be the equivalent of three or four servings. Eating too much food will create brain fog and indigestion and also lead to unhealthy weight gain.

Conclude the meal with ginger, peppermint, or chamomile tea. These choices will facilitate good digestion and prepare you for a good night's sleep.

Note: If you are in charge of planning the business dinner, choose a restaurant that makes eating in a high performance way easier.

"My biggest joy has been to see so many executives increase their awareness to make better nutritional choices, and then experience firsthand how great they can feel and perform. Tignum is not about deprivation. Instead, we believe that simple choices can collectively make a significant difference. Whether it is getting rid of brain fog, increasing energy levels, improving performance, or enhancing resilience ... I love that moment when our clients realize that what they ate made the difference."
Patti Milligan, Tignum Director of Nutrition

Airport Eating for High Performance

As noted previously, research has found that frequent travelers consume many more preservatives, chemicals, sugar, and trans fats than those who eat at home. This not only leads to unhealthy weight gain, but it also contributes to jet lag, frequent illness, and poor performance. The following tips are designed to help you make better choices and improve your performance while traveling:

Develop a travel food list. Taking some high performance snacks with you when you travel will prevent you from being at the mercy of the airport food and also help you avoid becoming too hungry. Suggestions for travel foods include:

_dried fruits (dried apricots, raisins, cranberries, mango, figs)
_whole fruits (bananas, oranges, apples, grapefruits)
_beef jerky
_nuts and seeds (almonds, sunflower seeds, pecans, soyanuts, walnuts)
_trail mixes or peanut butter pretzels
_ready-to-eat energy bars (follow the recommendations previously presented)
_carrots, celery, pea pods, or edamame (soy beans)

_instant oatmeal or other hot cereals (you can always find hot water and
  a cup to prepare it yourself)
_teas (green, ginger, chamomile)
_packets of Emergen-C supplement (source of Vitamin C, B vitamins,
  and minerals)

Start the trip with a good breakfast. This is the beginning of your trip, so start
it off with a nutritional breakfast that stabilizes your blood glucose and nour-
ishes your body and brain.

Stay hydrated. Airplanes are pressurized to an atmospheric pressure equal to
2,400 meters (8,000 feet), which can quickly dehydrate you. Making sure you
stay hydrated is crucial to preventing or reducing jet lag and keeping your
immune system healthy. Whenever possible, plan ahead by bringing your own
water bottle. Reduce or avoid caffeinated drinks, high-sugar drinks, and alcohol
since these will dehydrate you.

Eat every three to four hours. This will prevent blood glucose dips and excessive hunger. Remember that flights can be delayed, so don't count on the meal
on the airplane. Consider eating a small snack before boarding. You don't have
to eat the entire meal on the plane if everything goes as scheduled.

Avoid foods that are high in sugar or that have heavy sauces. If you need to
eat at the airport, avoid sugary pastries, sweetbreads, and doughnuts. These
foods disrupt blood glucose levels and do not add the nutrient-rich vitamins and
minerals needed for traveling. Select foods that provide you with a balance of
carbohydrates, protein, fat, and fiber.

Watch portion sizes. Airports and airplanes are like restaurants—each meal
usually exceeds our recommended portion size. Optimal lunch or dinner choices
include:

_grilled fish or chicken

_lean meats (lean pork stir-fry or small grilled hamburger)

_fresh green salad or steamed vegetables

_fruit and yogurt

_deli sandwiches on pita or flatbread

_beans or grilled meats and vegetables on whole wheat tortilla

_baked potato or sweet potato (with vegetable add-ons, salsa, and limited
  sour cream or butter)

High Performance Nutrition for Must-Win Events

*It's 2 pm and you're doing your final preparation for your client presentation
at 2:30. You ate a light lunch that consisted of a mixed green salad with seared
salmon, so you feel great. When you returned to the office, you made a couple
small changes to your slides, inspired by some thoughts you had while you were
walking back to the office. You double-checked your figures and spruced up your
fonts. You did your final research to be sure to understand your client's needs.
You've integrated all the what ifs you can imagine. You've gone through the
slides several times and completed your mental imagery to energize and focus
yourself.*

*You run to the bathroom one last time. On the way out, you stop by the small
kitchen to fill your water bottle. You notice the coffee left in the pot but you feel
energized, so it doesn't even tempt you. You get back to your desk and do a few
breathing squats and a quick posture check. (These strategies will be covered in
the next chapter.)*

*It's 2:21, time to unplug your laptop and head into the presentation. You grab
your strategic snack (almonds and dried cranberries), your water, your notes,
and your laptop. You head into the conference room, set up your laptop, take a
few deep breaths, do your final posture check, and smile, because you're ready
to go.*

In fact, you are 100% effectively prepared to deliver a winning performance!

Evaluate Your Nutrition Habits

Each person has a unique relationship with food, and this relationship impacts your nutritional habits. An important concept for sustainable high performance is becoming aware of your habits, your needs, and the benefits you get from your food. As you increase awareness of the way that you feel after you eat, you will experience a new motivation for improving your nutritional habits. The great thing about Nutrition is that you are only one meal away from getting back on track.

Do you want to sink, float, or swim?

The choice is always yours.

You have Nutrition habits that will make you **sink** if you:

_are unaware of why you eat, when you eat, and how much you eat
_eat fast food more than three times a week
_eat a diet that is high in processed foods
_rarely eat vegetables or fruit
_consistently eat until you are stuffed and uncomfortable
_wait to eat until you are starving
_drink soda as your beverage of choice at most meals
_rarely drink water (consciously)
_drink more than four cups of coffee or other caffeinated drinks every day
  and depend on these to wake up and stay awake or engaged in meetings
_drink more than three alcoholic drinks more than three days per week
_follow the 80–20 rule where 80 % of your food choices are indulgences
_consistently skip meals, especially at work
_fail to plan ahead for meetings, travel, and business dinners
_are unaware that Mindset, Nutrition, Movement, and Recovery habits
  impact your energy, resilience, brain performance, and capacity

You have Nutrition habits that will enable you to **float** if you:

_are aware of why you eat, when you eat, and how much you eat but only
    occasionally make better choices
_choose to eat the majority of your meals from frozen or prepackaged items
_eat processed meals or snacks more than four times per week
_occasionally eat vegetables and fruits
_often overeat to the point of being uncomfortably full
_eat high-sugar snacks on most days
_drink two or three sodas on most days
_drink three to four glasses of water a day
_need coffee or other caffeinated drinks to wake up or make it through
    the day on most days
_drink more than two alcoholic drinks on most days
_occasionally plan meals and snacks for your workday
_often work while you eat lunch
_eat in restaurants and make choices with no thought for high performance
    after the meal
_rarely prepare for meetings, travel, or business dinners by consciously
    implementing High Performance Nutrition strategies
_have limited awareness of the impact that your food has on your
    performance, rarely using Mindset, Nutrition, Movement, and Recovery
    habits to improve

You have Nutrition habits to **swim** if you:

_are always aware of why you eat, when you eat, and how much you eat; and you consciously use this information to make good Nutrition choices
_rarely, if ever, eat fast food
_balance meals and snacks with protein, healthy fats, and complex carbohydrates
_eat nutrient dense vegetables at almost every meal
_start every day with a high performance breakfast that includes protein and complex carbohydrates
_rarely overeat (stop eating when comfortably full regardless of outside influences)
_wake up and drink a glass of water and then drink water as your main drink of choice throughout the day
_limit coffee and other caffeinated beverages to no more than two per day
_limit alcohol to no more than one drink per day
_include strategic snacks in the planning of your workday
_never skip meals at work or away from work
_stick to our Tignum 80–20 Guideline, especially when eating out in restaurants where high performance is required after the meal
_strategically plan meals and snacks to maximize your performance
_prepare for meetings, travel, and business dinners by consciously selecting high performance foods and drinks
_effectively utilize Nutrition strategies, along with Mindset, Movement, and Recovery strategies to improve your energy, resilience, brain performance, and capacity

Develop Your Performance Nutrition Goals

The sustainable High Performance Nutrition strategies presented in this section are designed to be integrated with our Performance Mindset, Performance Movement, and Performance Recovery strategies. These Nutrition strategies alone will not necessarily make you a high performer or increase the sustainability of your performance. In fact, it is very unlikely that you will make High Performance Nutrition choices if you are overtired, do very little physical movement, or have a negative attitude. The four Tignum pillars of sustainable high performance are intricately interwoven and dependent upon each other. The true power of personal innovation comes with the integration of Mindset, Nutrition, Movement, and Recovery habits.

In order to take everything you have learned and create High Performance Nutrition, you need to develop Nutrition goals that are meaningful to you. To begin this process, consider the following questions:

What three action steps can you take now to help you improve your Nutrition?

If you were to have a High Performance Nutrition day, what would your eating and drinking choices be?

How will you keep hydrated throughout the day?

How will you use High Performance Nutrition strategies to positively impact your business luncheons and dinners, travel time, and must-win events?

How will you use Nutrition strategies to increase your energy, resilience, brain performance, and capacity for sustainable high performance?

Section IV
Without Movement You'll Never Swim

Performance Movement – utilizing physical motion to reduce pain, generate energy, increase resilience, improve brain performance, maximize capacity, and produce sustainable success

Chapter Eleven
Get Set to Swim

Chapter Twelve
Movement to Keep Swimming

Chapter Eleven
Get Set to Swim

"I used to think of movement as something that had to do with sports, fitness, or losing weight. I never thought it was relevant to improving my performance in my business. Most surprising to me is that when I do my Daily Prep movements in the morning, take the stairs every chance I get, and just move more, I am energized throughout the entire day. I stand taller, I feel better, and I am more confident and passionate.
These things aren't fitness-related. These are key pieces to the puzzle of being a high performer. Now I see movement completely differently. I can't imagine a day without doing some kind of movement. I use movement to get started in the morning, to get energized and focused for meetings, to take a break at lunch, and to unwind at the end of the day."
Tignum Client

The human body's ability to adapt to regular activity and exercise by becoming stronger, and more efficient, sustainable, and resistant to injury and illness exemplifies its unique design. The design of your anatomy from the type, location, and function of your joints and bones; to the layout and adaptability of your muscles; to the expansiveness of your circulatory system; to the complexity of your nervous system demonstrates that your body is meant to move.

Most people are aware that regular exercise has enormous health benefits, such as lowering cholesterol levels; decreasing the risk for heart disease, cancer, and diabetes; and reducing stress, high blood pressure, lower back pain, and obesity. A recent study published in the Archives of Internal Medicine has shown even more benefits. Did you know that by walking moderately or briskly for just 30 minutes for five or more days per week you can not only improve your fitness and quality of life, but also increase your life span an average of three-and-a-half years? Not only that, this study showed that these years were enjoyed almost heart-disease free, demonstrating that regular Movement definitely means higher quality and quantity of life.

Fewer people are aware that consistent Movement can also improve self-esteem and confidence, enhance left-right brain balance, increase mental ability and quality of sleep, and decrease depression. The most recent research on exercise and the brain may surprise you. Harvard Medical School has found that regular exercise (specifically aerobic exercise five days a week) stimulates the growth of new brain cells and may even prevent or slow the progress of Alzheimer's disease. Exercise has also been shown to stimulate and strengthen neurochemical brain functions. Clearly, Movement is not only great for the body—it is also great for the brain.

Many people are searching for that magic fountain of youth, and regular Movement can certainly contribute to that fountain. Regular Movement increases your heart's efficiency, the number of blood vessels feeding your heart, the amount of oxygen carried in your blood, as well as your self-esteem, creativity, and performance.

How Much Do You Move?

Starting today, begin expanding your awareness of your Movement. Pay attention to the type of Movement that you do on a daily basis. Do you take the elevator or do you take the stairs? When you are at the airport, do you take the people mover or do you walk? Do you drive around the parking lot looking for the closest parking space? How good is your balance? Can you touch your toes? These questions are important because they can provide you with a new awareness of your Movement habits and the impact that they have on your energy.

To build upon your awareness, consider the following:

Do you sit at your desk for hours at a time without getting up to take a walk, stretch, or do a couple of exercises?

Do you ignore how your body feels and the signals it gives you?

Do you resist getting daily Movement?

Your body adapts to activity and exercise by becoming stronger and enhancing your resistance to injury and illness. On the contrary, when you stop or limit your Movement, your body regresses into a multitude of illnesses. Lack of exercise also significantly affects your moods and diminishes your Quality of Time. In fact, there is a plethora of research that has shown specific health risks associated with leading a sedentary life. And, without regular Movement, your performance at work and away from work is diminished.

Experts also speculate that movements that require balance, coordination, rotation, rhythm, and multiplanar patterns may stimulate left-right brain integration. This makes logical sense since the left brain controls the right side of the body, and the right brain controls the left side of the body. Similarly, movements that require complex neurological involvement such as balancing, moving in multiple directions or planes, and integrating rhythm or coordination require a high level of feeling or proprioception (right brain), as well as feedback analysis (left brain). As noted previously, when both sides of your brain work together seamlessly, you will have a high performance brain.

At Tignum, we believe that any Movement system must be functional. That is, it must make you feel better, help you recover quicker, perform your activities of daily living easier, and allow you to fully enjoy life. Most exercise programs focus on how much muscle you can build, how many miles you can run, or how many hours you can spend in the gym. The fact is, if you can run 60 kilometers (37 miles) per week but you are exhausted, in pain, and frequently getting ill, you are off track. And, just because you have low body fat, bulging muscles, and a 90-minute, five-day-a-week weight training program does not mean that you are healthy and balanced on the inside.

The key to maximizing the benefits of Movement is to make it a daily habit. Few choices pay higher dividends in improving your performance than good Movement habits.

A Revolutionary Approach

The Tignum Performance Movement System is simple yet revolutionary. It focuses on the basic Movement patterns that are integrated into your neural programming. It combines movements and energy systems in a way to maximize impact while minimizing time. Our strategies are designed to enhance your brain function, improve your immune function, develop and strengthen your posture, rebalance your autonomic nervous system (ANS), build your capacity, improve your performance in your activities of daily living, increase your bone density, and enhance your neuromuscular system. Simply put, the Tignum Performance Movement System will improve your performance, at work and away from work.

What are the benefits of Movement?

Movement increases
_oxidation of fat
_number of coronary blood vessels
_efficiency of heart
_efficiency of peripheral blood distribution and return
_electron transport capacity
  fibrinolytic (clot-dissolving) capability
_arterial oxygen content
_red blood cells and blood volume
_thyroid function
_growth hormone production
_left-right brain balance
_creativity and mental focus
_self-esteem and confidence
_resilience to stress

Movement decreases

_serum cholesterol and triglycerides (blood fats)
_glucose tolerance (reducing your risk for diabetes)
_obesity
_platelet stickiness (inadvertent clotting)
_arterial blood pressure
_resting heart rate
_vulnerability to dysrhythmias (heart attacks)
_overreaction to hormones
_illness, injury, and risk for some diseases
_anxiety
_depression

Our philosophy on Movement is unique. We combine movements from tai chi, qigong, yoga, and competitive athletics. We recognize that for most corporate executives, time and equipment are hindering factors. We also understand that many people who travel extensively, sit in meetings, and work under high-stress conditions need Movement that rebuilds their body, rebalances their ANS, and refills their energy reserves. Our approach is to provide our clients with solutions that build the immune system; generate energy; improve brain performance, mobility, stability, and balance; and build capacity and strength in the least amount of time.

Movement Patterns of Daily Living

Every time you pick up your briefcase, suitcase, or your child, you must stabilize your trunk to protect your spine and to anchor the forces necessary to perform the task. Every time you run up a flight of stairs, run to catch a plane or bus, play tag with your child, or take a hike, you must engage a series of energy systems and your cardiovascular system to deliver the necessary energy to get the job done.

Although the demands of your daily life may vary from those of an athlete, your body still requires mobility, stability, balance, and strength, as well as endurance to perform at its best.

In order to perform the activities of daily living, there are basic Movement patterns that must be performed. All human movement is one, or a combination, of these:

_standing and locomotion (moving forwards, backwards, and side to side)
 raising/lowering center of mass
_pushing and pulling
_rotation

In order to move properly, without compensation or pain, you must be able to perform these basic Movement patterns efficiently with perfect posture. Unfortunately, too many people mindlessly go to the gym to add muscle mass or strength to dysfunctional Movement patterns, only to create an injury, pain, or fatigue. This is why we so firmly believe, as Gray Cook, author of Athletic Body in Balance, states: the key to all performance enhancement and injury reduction is good Movement patterns.

The Importance of Posture

A fundamental strategy for producing and managing energy, as well as reducing your risk of injury and illness, is to maintain good posture. Your body is designed to have a certain alignment with built-in curves and shock absorbers. When this alignment is altered, it affects every function of your body. It even affects your confidence and self-esteem. When your posture is in alignment, you have more energy because you are more efficient. When your posture is compromised, you begin a chain reaction of muscular tension that can drain your energy, affect your blood flow and nervous system function, and create pain. Many of your daily activities (e.g., sitting at a computer, driving a car, or walking in high heels) can alter your posture without you even being aware of it.

Posture is both static (without movement, as when you are sitting or standing) and dynamic (with movement, as when you are exercising). Your head is like a bowling ball weighing approximately 11 pounds (5 kilograms). Imagine the strain on your neck joints, ligaments, and muscles when your head is thrust forward, as is often the case when you are working on a computer.

You need to become aware of your posture at all times.

A place to start is: Think about your bowling ball (head) as you move throughout the day and work to keep this ball centered perfectly on a properly aligned support system.

In addition, perfect posture for the rest of your body means that your knees should be aligned over your ankles, your hips should be aligned over your knees, your shoulders should be aligned over your hips, and your ears should be aligned over your shoulders.

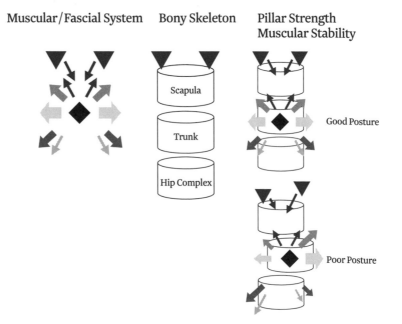

Adapted from graphic developed by Mark Verstegen from Athletes' Performance

The Tignum Performance Movement System

We have designed our system to increase your self-awareness of current Movement habits and to utilize the many opportunities to incorporate Movement into your daily schedule. We then focus on improving mobility, stability, and balance, which research has shown will reduce the risk of musculoskeletal injury and pain. This will also enable you to participate in a multitude of activities for daily living, ultimately enhancing your health, performance, and quality of life. Next, our system helps build your capacity through a highly effective and efficient method of cardiovascular training. The final level, designed to improve your functional strength, includes a circuit strength training program designed to improve function, strength, and endurance, and to reduce the risk of injury.

The four levels of our Tignum Performance Movement System include:

_Increase Blood Flow and Enhance Your Immune System
_Improve Your Mobility, Stability, and Balance
_Expand Your Capacity Through Energy System Development (ESD)
_Build Sustainability Through Functional Strength

In each level, we help leaders design and incorporate the most effective strategies for their individual needs. Much research has been done on each of these areas, but the important thing is that you understand these concepts and how easily they can be implemented into your daily life to improve your High Performance Movement habits.

Level 1 – Increase Blood Flow and Enhance Your Immune System

Wake up your body, release tension, and perform better.

The first level of Movement is a MUST. Often the excuse for not moving more is that there is not enough time. The truth is that there are a multitude of opportunities to move throughout your day. By simply taking advantage of these opportunities, you can easily keep moving to increase blood flow and enhance your immune system. Every time you move, your lymph flow is increased, which transports antigen-presenting cells and stimulates your immune response.

In this level, we encourage you to look for opportunities to move more on a daily basis. Make the choice to take the stairs rather than the escalator. Walk instead of using the automatic people-mover at the airport. Park farther from the entrances so that you can walk to your appointments. Perform some self-massage (see Tennis Ball Massage below) every day. Avoid sitting for long periods by going for a short walk or doing some stretches every 90 minutes or so. By setting your goals for Movement to happen every day, studies have shown that you will actually meet your goal at least five times a week.

Tennis Ball Massage

At Tignum, we love simple solutions with big impact. This is why we love the tennis ball. It's small, easy to carry, inexpensive, and it can help you reduce pain and tension, improve your blood flow, enhance your immune system, and even stimulate your right brain. Tennis ball massage is a simple and practical way to massage away your tension. It is a great way to start or end your day, take a break, or just release tension after a challenging meeting or event.

Practice

_Take off your shoes.

_Stand on one foot and place the tennis ball under your other foot.

_Now, slowly put your weight down on the ball and massage your foot in the process.

_Roll the ball forwards, backwards, side-to-side, and pay attention to any tender spots on your foot.

_Apply steady pressure for 10 to 30 seconds on each tender area until the pain starts to dissipate.

_Next, roll the ball all around the area that you massaged to circulate all of the waste products that were just released.

_Move on to the next spot.

_You can also use your tennis ball to explore your body for other tight and painful areas. Try using it on your neck, chest, thighs, calves, or anywhere that tension builds up in your body.

_Best of all, throw your tennis ball into your briefcase or suitcase, and you have your own traveling masseuse.

Level 2 – Improve Your Mobility, Stability, and Balance

Challenge your nervous and muscular system, develop your core, and re-balance your stress hormonal system to perform your best.

Building mobility, stability, and balance is also a MUST. For this level, we have designed Tignum Daily Prep, which combines movements from yoga, tai chi, qigong, and sports training. If you go through the Daily Prep movements a minimum of three times a week, you will not believe the impact it will have on your energy and productivity. This series of exercises takes less than 15 minutes and can be performed at any time during your day.

You can also incorporate Movement strategies from our Meeting Prep, which includes three simple movements that can be done in business attire, in your office, and in less than one minute.

Tignum Daily Prep provides fantastic full-body mobility, stability, and balance enhancement movements. Combining these with your breathing, you will enhance your energy flow and improve the oxygenation of your body and brain. These movements will challenge your neurological system, as well as your muscular system, which will also stimulate your right brain. In addition, this series of movements will have a restorative function for your immune system and will improve your ANS balance.

These movements are an excellent way to start your day, prepare for an activity, energize you anytime during the day, or help you eliminate stress and relax at the end of a hectic day. Many of our clients begin their Movement program by simply doing these movements. They gradually (over three weeks) build up to 10 repetitions of each movement and then suddenly find that they feel energized and motivated to do even more activities. For those who aren't doing any Movement at all, this is a good way to start and an effective gateway to better Movement habits.

Tignum Meeting Prep uses three simple movements to energize and focus you prior to a critical meeting. These movements reverse the detrimental effects of desk life and prepare your posture for high-impact or must-win events. These movements are also designed to stimulate your right brain to improve creativity.

When you have an upcoming presentation or meeting, your body is often full of stress and tension. The body's normal response is to want to fight or take flight. Performing a quick pre-performance set of movements before going into your event can reduce the impact of stress, enhance your creativity, eliminate nervous energy, and improve your self-esteem. All of these are crucial to performing your best.

Go to www.tignum.com/sinkfloatswim to view our Tignum Daily Prep and Meeting Prep movements, complete with visuals and in-depth instructions. Log in with the password "swimmer" to access these High Performance Movement strategies.

Consider the following:

What is your posture like and how can you improve it?

What can you do TODAY to move more?

What other activities would you love to do if you could improve your mobility, stability, and balance with your Daily Prep movements?

On a scale of 1-10, how committed are you to regular Movement?

Chapter Twelve
Movement to Keep Swimming

After developing your foundation (Movement patterns), improving your posture, and utilizing every opportunity in your day to move, you can now kick it into high gear to receive the maximum benefits of Movement. In this chapter, we will address how you can use Movement to increase your capacity and enhance your functional strength. We will assist you in achieving high performance in the most efficient and effective ways.

When many of our clients hear the word "exercise," they think of cardiovascular exercise, which usually means going for long runs or putting lots of kilometers or miles on their bicycles. Although this may be the way cardiovascular exercise has been done traditionally, at Tignum, we approach it much differently.

We understand that you usually have limited time or may not like long, strenuous workout sessions. By developing a time-efficient workout that fits your individual needs, we have created a way that you can experience all the benefits of cardio-vascular (aerobic) training, without an extensive time commitment. These benefits include:

_better health by reducing cardiovascular risk factors
 (e.g., body composition, blood lipid profile, blood pressure)
_reduced mental anxiety
_enhanced quality of sleep
_increased energy levels
_improved brain performance
_strengthened resilience
_weight management

Level 3 – Expand Your Capacity Through ESD

**Build your capacity with interval training to maximize
your performance.**

In this level, we introduce the Tignum ESD interval training program, which is a very efficient and effective method of cardiovascular exercise. Energy system development (ESD) is a model of training designed by our world-class partners at Athletes' Performance. It is an excellent way to develop your body's multiple energy systems, and High Performance Coach Paul Robbins uses these methods to train some of the most elite athletes in the world.

By utilizing these methods, you will maximize your energy, resilience, and capacity in the least amount of time. If you are committed to taking this next step, then implementing the Tignum ESD training program only two times a week for 20 to 30 minutes will give you outstanding benefits. Even if you're a person who usually hates cardiovascular training, you will find our approach appealing and fun.

At Tignum, the first step is to run our clients through a battery of evaluations. We use the iMETT Metabolic Cardiovascular Testing System, a specialized machine that measures aerobic fitness (oxygen consumption) and ventilatory threshold. These results provide us with the following valuable information for each individual, making it possible to design a customized training program:

_First, we get a clear picture of our clients' aerobic fitness. This evaluation tells us how well our clients' bodies can take oxygen from the air, transport it to the working muscles, and then use it to produce energy.

_Second, the evaluation provides us with the specific training heart rates that our clients should use during their various workout days. Each one of our Tignum clients leaves with an individually designed training program.

_Third, it shows us how well our clients can recover after pushing themselves. This gives us a snapshot of each person's level of resilience. If a person can push her/himself hard but recover quickly, we know that this is a highly resilient and extremely fit individual.

Energy Systems for Training

For the purpose of this book, we are going to provide you with an alternative method to determine your training heart rates for each energy system (zone). However, before we introduce this method, you need to understand what each heart rate zone represents.

Aerobic Energy System
The body has three main energy systems that it can utilize to provide energy when moving or breathing. The one that is most commonly known is the aerobic energy system (Zone 1) which is used to move at lower intensities. This energy system utilizes carbohydrates, proteins, and fats in the presence of ample amounts of oxygen to produce energy. The aerobic energy system is fairly efficient which means it produces very little waste (lactic acid), and therefore can be used for long distances or long periods of time.

This is the energy source that you use when you walk from the subway or go for an easy jog. This is also the energy system that long-distance runners, cyclists, or any other endurance athlete relies upon most.

Aerobic capacity is commonly reported as the VO2 max (maximum amount of oxygen you can utilize during intense exercise). The VO2 max varies significantly among individuals and is dependent upon genetics, age, gender, altitude, and of course, training. An average VO2 max for a person who does not exercise is approximately 35 ml/kg/min. In contrast, Lance Armstrong has been reported to have an aerobic capacity of 85ml/kg/min, which is almost twice that of an extremely fit 45-year-old male.

While even extensive training will not increase your aerobic capacity to Armstrong's level, consistent training will help improve your aerobic capacity. This becomes a very useful asset in recovering from the stress of business, especially when combined with training your other energy systems.

The Anaerobic Threshold

As the intensity of your efforts increase, there is a shift from using your aerobic energy system to using your anaerobic energy system. This occurs naturally and you will recognize it as the point where you starting breathing much deeper and faster, and find it challenging to hold a comfortable conversation. This point is called the anaerobic threshold (Zone 2) and is very important for interval training, as well as for improving your performance.

Anaerobic Energy System

The anaerobic energy system (Zone 3) is used for short bouts (from 10 seconds up to three minutes) of more intense Movement. This energy system is designed to produce energy in the absence of adequate oxygen, but not without a cost. The anaerobic energy system can only burn carbohydrates and protein (not fat) as an energy source, and to do so, produces the byproduct lactic acid. The accumulation of lactic acid leads to the burning sensation you feel in the exercising muscles.

This is the energy source that you use when you run up a flight of stairs or have to run fast to catch the train. Because your body builds up lactic acid when using this energy system, you are eventually forced to slow down or stop running if you continue at this high intensity.

ATP-PC System

The final energy system is used for short-duration, highly explosive movements such as lifting something heavy or jumping out of the way of a swerving car. This system is called ATP-PC (ATP stands for Adenosine Tri Phosphate) and will only provide you with energy for 10 seconds or less. You will train this energy system in Level 4 of the Tignum Performance Movement System when you implement our No Excuse Workout.

Benefits of ESD Training

ESD training uses an interval approach which trains the body to burn fats more efficiently and to recover more quickly. In addition, many of our clients find it mentally stimulating (with all the interval changes), less time-consuming, and considerably less boring and uncomfortable (since you only stay in each interval for a short time).

For executives who want the most benefit for the time invested, ESD training is the high performance solution. In just 15 minutes, you can begin to see and feel the benefits. In fact, many of our clients find that after just four weeks of ESD training, they recover quicker, fall asleep faster, feel more energetic, and are already getting leaner.

Too often, after traveling across time zones or attending high stress meetings, clients will go for a run which only compounds the level of stress on their ANS. Before using our ESD approach, they have shared that they would often get sick or overtired the day after pushing themselves too hard. Is this high performance? No, this is overtraining, and it is working hard rather than smart.

However, when clients monitor their heart rates, they quickly notice that in order to stay in their assigned heart rate zones they need to slow down, to take it easier. Does this mean they are being wimpy? No, not at all. Their heart rates are telling them that on that day, at that time, their bodies are not capable of pushing harder without overstressing themselves.

In our experience, this is one of the greatest benefits of using heart-rate-based ESD training. The heart rate monitor helps you adjust your training based upon your body's ability to handle the current demand placed upon it. This objective assessment is an excellent way to see if you are on the right track, doing too much, and how well you are recovering.

In utilizing ESD training, you will be
_training smart rather than training hard
_more motivated
_training multiple energy systems
_teaching your body to recover more quickly
_enabling your body to burn fat more efficiently
_burning more calories
_utilizing your time more efficiently

Estimate Your Heart Rate Training Zones

Although the most accurate method of determining your heart rates for the three training zones is to get tested, we are providing an alternative method to estimate your proper heart rates. Please remember that, as always, you should get clearance from your personal physician before starting any exercise program.

In the following chart, you will note that we included how to compute your training heart rates along with a description of what you should be feeling at that specific heart rate. We did this for two reasons. First, it will allow you to adjust your heart rates based upon how you feel (since this is only an estimate). Second, we included both so that you can use ESD training even if you don't have a heart rate monitor. Of course, this is not the most accurate way to train, but it is a simple and inexpensive method.

Training Zone	Formula	What You Should Feel	Benefits
Zone 1: Aerobic Energy System	Range between (220 – your age) x (multiply by) 0.65 to (220 – your age) x (multiply by) 0.75	You may initially feel winded, but in this zone you should be able to speak freely, even though you feel like you are putting forth some effort.	Expands your aerobic capacity which helps you recover, build your heart and lung capacity, and increase your efficiency in burning fats.
Zone 2: Anaerobic Threshold	Range between (220 – your age) x (multiply by) 0.75 to (220 – your age) x (multiply by) 0.85	You should feel like you have to shorten your sentences and you are beginning to feel winded. You should feel like you are pushing yourself a little beyond your comfort zone.	Increases your aerobic and anaerobic energy systems and ultimately helps you increase your anaerobic threshold which improves your performance.
Zone 3: Anaerobic Energy System	Range between (220 – your age) x (multiply by) 0.90 to (220 – your age) x (multiply by) 0.92	You should feel like you are really working and breathing hard. You should feel like it's difficult to hold a conversation.	Increases your physical speed and power, speeds up your metabolism, and teaches your body to efficiently burn carbohydrates and fats (during recovery).

As an example, let's imagine that you are 48 years old. To complete the Aerobic Energy System (Zone 1) equations, you would use:

$(200 - 48)$ x $0.65 = 152$ x $0.65 = 98.8$
(the minimum number for your heart rate in this zone)

$(200 - 48)$ x $0.75 = 152$ x $0.75 = 114$
(the maximum number for your heart rate in this zone)

Therefore, the heart rate range for your Training Zone 1 is approximately 99 to 114 beats per minute.

"I used to gauge my running only on how fast I thought I should be running. If I was tired, I would push myself as hard as I could to keep my predetermined pace. When I started heart-rate-based training, I quickly learned that there were many times that I was pushing myself too hard and also a few times when I could have pushed myself harder.

My heart rate monitor gives me insights into what my body is capable of in the moment and then it helps me adjust the intensity of my exercise to match it. Since using my heart rate monitor, along with the Tignum ESD program, I have run my personal best 10K and half marathon. Even more important to me, I haven't gotten sick or injured one time."
Tignum Client

How to Implement ESD Training

Once you have computed your three sets of training zone heart rates, you are ready to get started. Even though it is not required, we recommend that you purchase a heart rate monitor to make your training sessions as effective and productive as possible.

Stage One ESD Training:
for beginners, unconditioned individuals, or anyone who has not done ESD training before.

_Start slowly and gradually build up to 20 to 60 minutes of Movement in Zone 1. This can be done by walking, jogging, hiking, swimming, rowing, bicycling, or any form of Movement that you enjoy. The longer you move, the more calories you will burn, but please don't feel pressured to do more and more time.

_In the beginning, you may only be able to stay in Zone 1 for 5 minutes. Remember, even a marathon can be run 5 minutes at a time. The big thing is to get moving and to not let your heart rate go above your Zone 1 range.

_If your heart rate begins creeping up, simply slow down (maybe even walk slowly) until it drops into your Zone 1 range.

_Similarly, be sure to not let your heart rate fall below your Zone 1 range if you can.

_Ideally, you should repeat Stage One Training three to five times a week.

Stage Two ESD Training:
for those people who have completed Stage One or have some experience with ESD training and a moderate level of fitness.

_Begin with a warm-up in Stage One for 5 minutes. During this warm-up, you should gradually increase the intensity to get your heart rate into your Zone 1 range, but not above it.

_At the 5-minute mark, increase the intensity of your Movement (for 2 minutes) so that your heart rate increases to your Zone 2 range. It's not critical where it is as long as it is within the range. If your heart rate begins to go too high, simply slow down and reduce the intensity so that your body can lower your heart rate.

_At the end of 2 minutes in Zone 2, slow down and reduce your intensity for 3 minutes so your heart rate can return to your Zone 1 range. Be sure not to let your heart rate fall below your Zone 1 range. Make a mental note of how quickly your heart rate returns to your Zone 1 because your ultimate goal will be to recover faster.

_Repeat this sequence of Zone 2 (2 minutes) and Zone 1 (3 minutes) for as much time as you have in this training session. Preferably you can repeat this sequence three to five times.

_At the end of your session, be sure to end with 3 to 5 minutes in Zone 1 for a cool-down.

Stage Three ESD Training:
for those people who have completed Stage Two ESD training or are very fit.

_Begin with a warm-up in Stage One for 5 minutes. During this warm-up, you should gradually increase the intensity to get your heart rate into your Zone 1 range but not above it.

_At the 5-minute mark, increase the intensity of your Movement (for 1 minute) so that your heart rate increases to your Zone 2 range. It is not critical where it is as long as it is within the range. If your heart rate begins to go too high, simply slow down and reduce the intensity so that your body can lower your heart rate.

_At the end of 1 minute in Zone 2, increase your Movement intensity for an additional 30 seconds. Initially, your heart rate may not reach your Zone 3 range but with some practice, it will.

_At the end of your 30 seconds in Zone 3, slow down and reduce your intensity for 2 minutes so your heart rate can return to Zone 1. Be sure not to let your heart rate fall below your Zone 1 range. Make a mental note how quickly your heart rate returns to your Zone 1 range because your ultimate goal will be to recover faster.

_Repeat this sequence of Zone 2 (1 minute), Zone 3 (30 seconds) and Zone 1 (2 minutes) for as much time as you have in this training session. Preferably, repeat this sequence three to five times.

_At the end of your session, be sure to end with 3 to 5 minutes in Zone 1 for a cool-down.

Perfection Is Not a Worthy Goal
I often meet high performers that think that the only satisfaction they can ever celebrate and enjoy is being perfect. While I'm a huge advocate of never-ending improvement, I'm a firm believer that nothing destroys progress like perfectionism. I have found that behind most perfectionists is an underlying fear that is neither healthy nor productive.
When I work with clients who are in the process of their personal innovation, the ones who are most successful are the ones who successfully manage their fears. The biggest fear that must be overcome is the fear that they may not accomplish every goal they have set. Although this fear is normal, especially in the beginning, I try to help them realize that every step towards their goal is an accomplishment.
I remember one client who rated her day on Movement only 5 on a scale of 10, because she only got to run five miles and she wanted to run eight miles. On a perfect day (a fictional thing that really doesn't exist), her goal may have been to run eight miles; yet, on that busy and chaotic day, her accomplishment of running five miles was truly amazing. The problem is that with her old thinking she would have skipped the five-mile run because it was short of her "perfect" goal.
However, once she overcame her fear of not being perfect, she learned to take each day in stride and to celebrate each step she made towards her personal innovation. Several months later, she ran her personal best half marathon but even more importantly, she had achieved most of her goals in Mindset, Nutrition, and Recovery, as well.
Performance living is about setting meaningful goals, developing a reasonable and achievable plan, training smart rather than hard, being consistent in doing simple things savagely well, and celebrating and enjoying your progress towards your potential.
Overcoming any fears you may have of not being perfect is the first step towards a new level of performance living that you will truly enjoy.
Tignum Blog

Level 4 – Build Sustainability Through Functional Strength

Be prepared for your daily demands and sustain your high performance.

In this level, we introduce the Tignum strength workout to build the functional strength that you can use to make your activities of daily living easier. This workout is designed to help you develop or maintain your muscle mass so that you can increase your metabolism and decrease your risk of injury. We also call it our No Excuse Workout since it is time-efficient, involves minimal equipment, and can be done anywhere.

In strength training there is a term "absolute strength," which represents the absolute number of pounds (kilograms) that can be lifted one time. For power-lifters and some strength-based sports this may be necessary, but for executives, it's probably not. This is why we work with and use the term functional strength in Level 4 of our Tignum Movement System. "Functional strength" is about making it easier for you to perform your activities of daily living.

Daily living activities may include climbing stairs, getting in and out of your car, lifting a box in the office, or carrying your child at home. The smart approach is to spend the time to build the strength that you will need to be more efficient everywhere in your life. Nothing more and nothing less.

This type of functional training, through our No Excuse Workout, provides you with all of the benefits of traditional strength (resistance) training such as:

_increased muscular strength and muscular endurance
  enhanced bone density
_faster metabolism
_improved body composition

It also improves your coordination, core stability, and calorie expenditure while reducing your risk of getting injured and suffering from joint pain. This means that you not only move more efficiently, but it takes less effort for you to perform your activities of daily living. This leaves more energy for you to perform at work, as well as away from work.

We have found that many executives have not done any strength (resistance) Movement prior to working with Tignum. Because of this, their muscle mass has markedly decreased since they were in their mid-20s. For females, this decrease is often more exaggerated because they don't have the levels of testos-terone that males have. This may not seem like a big deal, but it actually is more significant than you may realize. Muscle mass is a major contributor to your basal metabolic rate. This means the more muscle mass you have, the more calories you will burn 24 hours a day, seven days a week, 52 weeks a year.

The American Council on Exercise proclaims: "For each decade after the age of 25, 3-5% of muscle mass is lost." This is due to changes in lifestyle and a decreased use of the neuromuscular system. However, studies have shown significant gains in previously sedentary older adults following a program of regular strength training. In short, if you don't use it, you will lose it. But more importantly, if you begin now, you can turn back the atrophying effects of age.

Our No Excuse Workout uses minimal equipment so you can complete it anywhere. Whether you're on the road, stuck in your office, or at home, with a couple of bands or portable rubber tubes, you can complete our entire workout. This doesn't mean that you can't use weights or other equipment, but it does mean that it isn't a requirement.

Our system is also time-efficient. We realize that you are usually stretched thin for time. Therefore, we designed our program to use your time effectively and to actually deliver the benefits that, in some programs, require hours of exercise to achieve. By using full body exercises with a circuit design, you will not only develop better functional strength but also burn more calories and develop additional cardiovascular conditioning.

In our approach, every exercise trains your entire body from your legs to your core to your upper body. This is the way your body works in the real world, so we believe it should be trained this same way. It is also the reason why you will notice immediate benefits in your Movement for daily activities.

Integrate the Tignum Levels of Movement

A frequent question that we are asked is how often to incorporate these four Tignum Levels of Movement. Our answer is two-fold and based upon your answers to the following questions:

What is your current level of overall stress?

What benefits do you wish to attain?

If your overall level of stress is high and you feel overwhelmed, exhausted, apathetic, unable to sleep well, short-fused, or extremely unfit, then you should remain in Level 1 and Level 2 until you begin to feel better. You can perform these levels every day, and you will see and feel the results within a couple of weeks.

Once you are feeling better, or if you are full of energy and have good health to begin with, we recommend that you implement all four levels immediately. Contrary to what you might think, this will not take a huge amount of time, but it will require some consistency. The following are Tignum recommendations on how often to incorporate these levels of Movement into your weekly schedule:

Level 1 – Increase Blood Flow and Enhance Your Immune System, **Daily**

Level 2 – Improve Your Mobility, Stability, and Balance
Three to five times a week (15 minutes each session)

Level 3 – Expand Your Capacity Through ESD
Two to five times a week (15 to 30 minutes each session)

Level 4 – Build Sustainability Through Functional Strength
Two to three times a week (10 to 30 minutes each session)

Go to www.tignum.com/sinkfloatswim and log in with the password "swimmer" to view the specific exercises in our No Excuse Workout and our recommendations for the integration of Tignum Levels of Movement.

Evaluate Your Movement Habits

Whether you're an athlete or not, the fact is that your body was built to move. If you lead a sedentary life, there is no way that you are generating the energy, resilience, brain performance, and capacity that you need. The Tignum program is not about becoming a triathlete, a marathoner, a competitive athlete, or even a fitness buff. It is about making the link between your brain and your body, achieving your potential, and feeling and performing better both at work and away from work. Too often people see Movement as something they did when they were younger, but now it is just too difficult, too time-consuming, or just a nice-to-do. Nothing can be further from the truth.

Do you want to sink, float, or swim?

The choice is always yours.

You have Movement habits that will make you **sink** if you:

_avoid moving at all costs
_take the elevator even if you are just going up one flight of stairs
_always circle the parking lot looking for the closest parking spot
_always use the people-mover at the airport rather than walk
_sit at your desk for more than two hours at a time without getting up to move
_sit for an entire flight rather than getting up and stretching
_do not do any regular Movement or stretching at all
_are consistently in pain and don't do anything about it
_can't bend over and touch your toes while keeping your legs straight
_can't walk up one flight of stairs without being out of breath
_have trouble getting in and out of your car
_watch more than five hours of television on weekend days
_ignore the signs that your body sends you regarding under- or overdoing it
_never use Movement to prepare for meetings
_are unaware that Movement is linked to your work performance
_only perceive Movement as related to health

You have Movement habits to enable you to **float** if you:

_are aware of opportunities to move but rarely act on them
_take the stairs only when you have to
_sometimes park farther away so that you have to walk, but not often
_usually take the people-mover at the airport, but not always
_sometimes sit for more than two hours before getting up to move
_only get up occasionally during long flights to stretch and move
_do regular Movement only two to three times per week
_stretch only when you're sore
_do some (resistance) strength training but inconsistently
_only do Movement activities on weekends
_plan to get Movement in regularly but then don't make it a priority,
  so it usually doesn't happen
_only do cardiovascular training but no resistance (strength) or mobility
  Movement
_only do resistance (strength) training
_jump into an exercise program that is way over your head
_set exercise goals such as a marathon or half marathon, but then train
  only partially or improperly
_train hard rather than smart
_believe that if there is no pain, there is no gain
_occasionally prepare for meetings by using Movement
_perceive Movement as somewhat important but don't make its connection
  to performance

You have Movement habits to swim if you:

_always look for opportunities to move and do it
_choose to take the stairs whenever possible rather than the elevator or escalator
_choose to walk rather than use the people-mover at airports
_rarely sit for more than 90 minutes before getting up to move
_regularly get up during long flights to stretch and move
_use Movement daily to increase blood flow, enhance immune function, and reduce pain
_activate your nervous system with a morning Movement routine at least five days per week
_use self-massage techniques on most days to eliminate muscle pain and tension and to improve blood flow
_integrate Movement to improve mobility, stability, and balance into your daily schedule
_use functional resistance training two to three times per week
_use interval training at least two times per week
_train smart rather than hard
_are aware of the signals your body sends you regarding the need for Movement and rest
_prepare for almost all meetings by energizing yourself with some Movement
_recognize that Movement is linked to your brain performance and your overall performance
_integrate Movement with Mindset, Nutrition, and Recovery strategies to improve and sustain your high performance at work and away from work

Develop Your Performance Movement Goals

The sustainable High Performance Movement strategies presented in this chapter are designed to be integrated with our Performance Mindset, Performance Nutrition, and Performance Recovery strategies. These Movement strategies alone will not necessarily make you a high performer or increase the sustainability of your performance. In fact, the limiting factor of overcoming most sedentary habits is developing the right Mindset. If you can't envision yourself as loving to move, it won't happen. The four Tignum pillars of sustainable high performance are intricately interwoven and dependent upon each other. The true power of personal innovation comes with the integration of Mindset, Nutrition, Movement, and Recovery habits.

In order to take everything you have learned and create High Performance Movement, you need to develop Movement goals that are meaningful to you. To begin this process, consider the following questions:

What three action steps can you take now to help you improve your Movement?

If you were to have a High Performance Movement day, what kinds of activities would you incorporate?

How will you use High Performance Movement strategies to positively impact your business meetings and must-win events?

How will you use Movement strategies to increase your energy, resilience, brain performance, and capacity for sustainable high performance?

Section V
Without Rest We All Sink

Performance Recovery – purposefully oscillating and regenerating to develop your energy, resilience, brain performance, and capacity to enhance your passion and purpose and produce sustainable success

Chapter Thirteen
Regenerate and Recharge to Swim

Chapter Fourteen
Sleep, Breathe, and Laugh to Swim

Chapter Fifteen
Swimming Is A Rhythm

Chapter Thirteen
Regenerate and Recharge to Swim

The unchallenged myth that only the weak need recovery has contributed to the downward spiral of productivity and explosive burnout rates in the business world.

When you look at top athletes and what prevents them from achieving their potential, you will rarely find that they aren't working hard enough. They may not always be working on the right things, but they are usually working as hard as they can. Instead, what they usually are not doing is paying enough attention to their Recovery and regeneration. This prevents their bodies and minds from benefiting from the training they are doing.

The same is true in the business world. Often high performing executives think of Recovery as something that only the weak need. This myth has helped fuel the increasing loss in productivity, decreasing effectiveness and performance, and rising burnout rates. By shifting paradigms and defining Recovery as a critical performance strategy, burnout can be prevented and sustainable high performance can be achieved.

When you walk into the Arizona training facility of our world-class training partner Athletes' Performance, the first thing you notice is that there is an area dedicated to work and an area dedicated to rest. Do they create this rest area because their athletes are lazy and need a place to lie around? Of course not. They have created space for both work and Recovery because they understand that physiologically the body (and the mind) requires adequate rest to perform its best. In other words, rest is a strategic part of their high performance formula.

Make Recovery a Strategic-Must

Ironically, when you look at the business world, there is very little understanding of the physiological need for Recovery. Even the best business schools in the world are just beginning to comprehend that working harder and harder is not necessarily sustainable or more productive. But unlike Athletes' Performance, these schools have not yet recognized Recovery as a strategic-must.

When you hear the word "recovery," you may think of taking a vacation, working less hours, or just saying no to new projects. Or perhaps recovery for you means a program that people go through when they have an addiction and want to get better. Our clients' initial responses to recovery are even more illuminating.

Many feel that Recovery is:

_for weak people
_something to worry about when they hit the wall
_for lazy people
_for people who aren't very busy
_for people who aren't real go-getters
_totally unproductive time
_a form of procrastination

However, we disagree with these responses and firmly believe that Recovery is an essential component of sustainable high performance. And so, we must re-iterate: **Recovery is a strategic-must.**

Just as a Formula One car must make pit stops if it wants to win, so must a high performing executive. But just like a race car, these executive "pit stops" must be quick, highly productive, and strategic. The Recovery strategies that we have developed are just that—time-efficient and effective—done in your office, sitting in a meeting, or standing in line at the airport. We see Performance Recovery as an integral part of working smart.

Because of the many preconceived negative ideas about Recovery, it is important to first focus on your Mindset. In order to change your thoughts, and ultimately your habits, you need to consider all the benefits that Performance Recovery strategies will give you. These benefits include:

_improved energy
_decreased muscle tension and joint pain
_strengthened immune function
_heightened clarity
_enhanced mood stability
_increased creativity (right-brain functioning)
_expanded capacity
_better job satisfaction
_more passion for life!

Which of these benefits will personally help you to be more productive, at work and away from work?

Do you strategically plan for your Recovery or do you leave it chance?

How do you know when you need more Recovery?

In 1931, Dr. Hans Selye developed the General Adaptation Syndrome (GAS), which described the disastrous performance and health consequences of being placed under constant stress without adequate and frequent Recovery. He also introduced the concept of oscillation where a person who is stressed is then provided strategies to fully recover from these periods of stress.

Further research by Selye led to the development of the supercompensation theory (commonly used in peak performance). Researchers have found that when people are placed under a progressive stress overload interlaced with active Recovery periods, they not only recover to their previous levels, but actually recover at higher (more advanced) performance levels. This discovery has led to the current periodized (or oscillating) method of training athletes, in which Recovery is considered as important as the intensity and amount of overload (training).

*"I have attended several high performance programs. They all stressed the need to get more
motivated, to push yourself harder, and to work through the pain (no pain – no gain approach).
I was always excited after these programs, but my motivation died out because the strategies
just weren't sustainable.*
*I think my biggest take-away from Tignum is how important recovery is for my performance.
I always thought that taking a break was something that my weaker colleagues needed. Now, I
realize that making my personal recovery a priority is the most important thing that I can do
to be a sustainable high performer. It is the foundation of my performance.*
*Since adding a few simple and short recovery breaks, I feel more productive, more focused,
and definitely less stressed. It has also been funny to see my colleagues' reactions because the
last thing they ever thought they'd see was a workaholic like me taking a break to go for a
short walk or do a breathing technique. But even they admit that they like this new me. I'm
way less reactive, much calmer, easier to be around, and I definitely get more done."*
Tignum Client

What Are You All Stressed Out About?

Whether you are an athlete or a corporate executive, one of the main factors to
how well you can perform and how long you can sustain your performance is
dependent upon how well you can recover from stress. The first step to implementing Performance Recovery strategies is to understand where your stress
comes from.

Often people are unaware of how much stress they are under. There are many
different types of stressors that affect your overall stress load and challenge your
autonomic nervous and hormonal systems to remain in balance. Becoming
aware of where your stress is coming from is essential to being able to develop
your own Recovery strategies.

Stressors

Environmental:
_temperature extremes >32 °C or <0 °C
_humidity > 60% or <20%
_altitude change (any change over 300 meters in past week)
_pollution (air, water, electromagnetic fields)

Psychological / Social:
_conflicts with boss or co-worker
_overwhelmed at work
_organizational change (policies, procedures, focus)
_change of job
_change in living arrangement
_doing home improvements
_attending school
_boredom
_lack of true friends/support
_lack of fun and enjoyment
_taking a vacation
_new baby
_child going to college
_separation or divorce
_family member in poor health
_loss of a family member or close friend
_mortgage 80-90% of market value
_high debt

Physiological / Biochemical:
_high-sugar diet
_high-gluten diet
_low-protein diet
_taking prescription or over-the-counter medications
_asthma
_cold or flu
_intestinal parasites
_fungal infection (yeast, athlete's foot)
_diabetes
_high blood pressure
_sleep deprivation
_sleep disorder (apnea, restless leg syndrome)
_alcohol (more than 14 drinks/week)

Anatomical / Structural:
_poor posture
_current injury
_lower back or neck pain
_any consistent pain
_recent surgery
_intense exercise > 4 days/week

In reviewing this list, consider where your stress comes from:

Which three stressors produce the most stress for you?

What additional sources of stress do you have in your life?

What are you currently doing to manage these stressors?

Can you manage all of your current stressors?

Recognize the Stress Cycle

Our bodies are built for short intermittent bursts of stress. With each stressor, the body responds to enhance its chances of high performance and short-term survival. The system is perfectly designed as long as your body gets adequate Recovery between bouts of stress to rebuild itself. In fact, acute stress makes you stronger, but chronic stress (an absence of Recovery) tears you down. The stress response is a combination of the nervous and endocrine systems' responses through a complex system called the HPA (hypothalamic-pituitary-adrenal) axis. This axis is not designed for constant stress, but rather for short bursts of stress with adequate Recovery. During this Recovery, the hormones are rebalanced and the feedback receptor sensitivity is reset.

Selye identified the stress cycle and its relationship to the HPA axis when he saw people getting ill from the stress they experienced during the tough times of the depression. In 1956, he published a book, which has since been updated and re-published, called The Stress of Life. Selye proposed a three-stage response to stress—alarm, resistance, and exhaustion—and described an array of illnesses caused by stress.

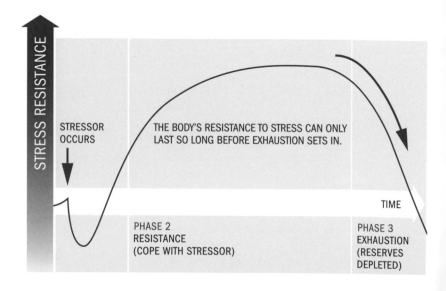

STRESS RESISTANCE

STRESSOR
OCCURS

THE BODY'S RESISTANCE TO STRESS CAN ONLY
LAST SO LONG BEFORE EXHAUSTION SETS IN.

TIME

PHASE 2
RESISTANCE
(COPE WITH STRESSOR)

PHASE 3
EXHAUSTION
(RESERVES
DEPLETED)

The Alarm Phase

People experience stress differently in their bodies. Some feel it as neck or back tightness or pain. Some may experience indigestion or heartburn. Still others get headaches or ringing in the ears (tinnitus). The more aware you are of where your body feels stress, the better you will become at responding early to rebalance your autonomic nervous system.

Symptoms of the Alarm Phase include:
_increase in heart rate
_increase in respirations
_decrease in pain
_heightened awareness
_improved focus
_improved performance

The Resistance Phase

Initially, the body responds perfectly to stress, and in fact, performance is enhanced. If there is an opportunity to oscillate (recover from the stress), performance continues to be enhanced and the body remains healthy. If there is not adequate Recovery, performance is compromised and the body will move into the resistance phase.

As you move into resistance, symptoms include:
_dry mouth and skin
_nervous stomach or heartburn
_tiredness
_breaks in concentration
_difficulty falling asleep
_early morning wake-ups with racing thoughts
_sweet cravings
_coffee cravings

_agitated feelings
_decreased patience
_slight depression

**Moving further into resistance but not quite into exhaustion,
symptoms include:**
_nervousness, shakiness, cold feeling
_heart palpitations
_lightheadedness when quickly standing up
_constipation with occasional diarrhea
_frequent wake-ups during middle of night or insomnia
_difficulty getting up in the morning
_food cravings (high in sugar, fat, and salt)
_coffee cravings
_alcohol cravings
_lethargic except immediately after eating
_weight gain (especially around the waist)
_amenorrhea (women)
_decreased immune system (get more frequent colds, flu, skin lesions)
_inability to recover from exercise (muscle and joint pain, tired muscles)
_unexplainable fatigue even after a good night of sleep
_unexplained muscular pain syndromes (low back pain, neck pain,
  elbow pain)
_decreased sex drive
_mood swings
_apathy
_overreactive temper
_brain fog
_avoidance of conflict or challenge

The Exhaustion Phase
The problem is that with constant stress, your HPA axis may remain out of balance, and you sink, sometimes permanently, into the exhaustion phase. At this stage, cortisol levels are so high feedback loops become less sensitive, and you become more susceptible to these imbalances. Prolonged stress specifically devastates the endocrine, cardiovascular, gastrointestinal, neurological, and immune systems. High blood cortisol levels also disrupt the circadian rhythms and elevate blood glucose levels, both of which further fatigue. This may ultimately lead to chronic fatigue, chronic inflammatory diseases, and even death.

As you move into exhaustion (burnout), symptoms include:
_myocardial contractures (permanent deformation of heart muscle cells)
_illness, some of which is possibly irreversible (ulcers, tinnitus, diabetes,
  hypertension, chronic fatigue, fibromyalgia, cancer, dementia, and
  congestive heart failure)
_loss of memory
_depression
_sudden death

The following client story highlights how even minor stress can turn into burnout if you fail to take Recovery breaks and don't pay close attention to the symptoms:

"When I developed burnout I never saw it coming. I didn't go through a major event such as a divorce, a job loss, or a death in my family. I had the 'normal' stress of being a corporate comptroller. As I eventually found out from my doctor, my problem was that I simply never got a break. I just went from one project, one stressor, to the next.

To make matters worse, because it gradually accumulated, I never paid attention to the stress in my body. It snuck up on me. Had I been more aware of what I was feeling, I would have recognized the danger I was in.

I am a high potential in my company and I have always been a high performer. I was the last person I ever thought would experience burnout."

The ANS Balancing Act

Your body has a nervous system that automatically deals with everything that is going on at this moment. This is called the autonomic nervous system (ANS), which is made up of a sympathetic nervous system (the gas pedal) and a parasympathetic nervous system (the brakes). The balance of these systems is critical to maintaining your energy and arousal levels, your physical response to stress, and ultimately your performance and health.

These two primary systems, the sympathetic and the parasympathetic, both have a purpose and a function. When a stress (challenge) occurs, the sympathetic nervous system quickly prepares your body to respond. It does this by immediately causing the release of adrenaline (epinephrine and norepinephrine) which increases heart rate, blood pressure, respiratory rates, and focus. It also causes the release of the stress hormone cortisol to help reduce pain and inflammation. All of this is designed for the short-term immediate response to fight or run from a stressor.

Sympathetic
_fight or flight (or freeze)
_break down for action
_trade the long-term needs for immediate needs

The parasympathetic nervous system keeps everything in check. It is responsible for relaxation, regeneration, and restoring the body to its pre-stress condition.

Parasympathetic
_rest and digest
_build up for the next fight or flight
_recovery for long-term needs

Neither system is good or bad; in fact, they are both needed. Your body works to stay in balance, but current work environments and societal demands tend to over-stimulate your sympathetic system and under-stimulate your parasympathetic system. This imbalance robs your body of energy and weakens your

immune system. Remember that the immune system is built for a long-term response from diseases that take time to develop. However, it will be sacrificed for
a more immediate short-term emergency if necessary.

Many people talk about stress management, and it's even become a cliché to say
to someone: "You must be under too much stress." The problem is that this
statement doesn't take into account that you cannot always control (or manage)
the challenges and demands that you face on a daily basis. And sometimes, telling
people to manage their stress becomes an additional stressor.

This is why we think it's really more about ANS balance. It's about working with
the framework of how your body is built to respond to the stressors you face.
Our strategies are all designed to synergistically create ANS balance, which will
ultimately help you have sustainable high performance, more energy, and better
health.

Stress to Perform Your Best

*Every day I turn on the news, and there is always a story about fighting stress or how to avoid
having too much stress in your life. The problem with this approach is that it fails to recognize
that we actually need stress.*
We need stress? Does this shock you?
*That's right. We need stress to perform our best. In fact, the body is designed to meet challeng-
es with energy, focus, passion, and power. There is an excellent description of this response in
Mihály Csíkszentmihályi's bestselling book Flow: The Psychology of Optimal Experience.
He succinctly describes flow—a high performance state where peak performance is unconscious
and even effortless. In the athletic world, it is sometimes known as being in the zone.
Interestingly enough, one of the most important components of getting into your flow is to
have a challenge greater than your norm. And, what is a challenge greater than your norm?
It's stress. You got it—stress can bring out the best in you.
What an interesting paradox: The key to sustainable high performance and getting in the flow
is not to eliminate stress. Instead, you need to create Mindset, Nutrition, Movement, and
Recovery habits that will ensure the positive use of stress for sustainable high performance.
How good are your habits?*
Tignum Blog

The Tignum Performance Recovery System

Our system focuses on teaching practical strategies to rebalance the ANS to avoid adrenal insufficiency, exhaustion, or collapse, and to support the brain and the body for high performance. The foundation of this work is increasing self-awareness to the body's natural oscillatory cycles such as the sleep cycle and circadian rhythms.

So, how can you perform your best even when you're under intense pressure? The key is to implement strategies that will maximize your body's normal rhythms.

Our Tignum Performance Recovery System is designed to do just that and consists of three levels:

_Eliminate Sleep Deprivation
_Rebalance and Reenergize
_Strategically Oscillate

In each level, we help leaders design and incorporate the most effective strategies for their individual needs. Much research has been done on each of these areas, but the important thing is that you understand these concepts and how easily they can be implemented into your daily life to improve your High Performance Recovery.

Consider the following:

How do you define Recovery?

How do you know when you need a Recovery break?

When are the best times in your day to implement Recovery breaks?

Chapter Fourteen
Sleep, Breathe, and Laugh to Swim

If there was a magic pill that could improve your performance, raise your energy level, improve your mental alertness, enhance your immune system, slow the aging process, help prevent obesity, and reduce the risk of premature death, would you take it?

The fact is that there is such a pill and you take it every night. It's called sleep but unfortunately you probably take too little. In fact, research suggests that 74% of adults report that they do not get enough sleep and 46% may have significant sleep deprivation.

Level 1 – Eliminate Sleep Deprivation

Sleep is nature's way of regularly providing regeneration to the brain and the body. This first level includes strategies to help you fall asleep, as well as improve your quality of sleep.

During the first three hours of sleep, your body secretes the greatest amount of growth hormone to help itself repair the damage that occurred throughout the day. This may explain why it is so exhausting to be awakened during the initial stage of sleep. Early researchers believed that sleep cycles occurred every 90 minutes and that healthy sleep should therefore fit into these 90-minute blocks.

Current sleep research shows, however, that sleep cycles actually vary throughout the night, with the first and final stages lasting close to an hour, and the middle stages lasting up to two hours. This finding is important because in its quest to eliminate sleep debt, the body actually adjusts the length and number of sleep cycles based upon its needs each night. This is why consistent sleep patterns (bedtime and wake time) are the most conducive to restorative sleep, and inconsistent sleep patterns (like those of a traveling corporate executive) are the most likely to lead to sleep deprivation.

Business Travel Statistics (British Airways, July 2005):
How has lack of sleep from business travel affected work?
_23% of business travelers stated that they fell asleep in a meeting
_18% stated that a presentation went badly
_14% missed a meeting or flight

Following are some general tips to help you fall asleep quickly and improve the quality of your sleep:

Go to bed and awaken at the same time every day including weekends. When you alter your bedtime, you often awaken in the middle of a sleep cycle and do not feel refreshed. A regular waking time in the morning strengthens the circadian function and can help with sleep onset at night.

Establish a regular, relaxing bedtime routine such as breathing exercises, reading a book, or listening to soothing music. A relaxing, routine activity right before bedtime conducted away from bright lights helps separate your sleep time from activities that can cause excitement, stress, or anxiety. Avoid arousing activities before bedtime like working, paying bills, engaging in competitive games, or family problem-solving. In addition, avoid exposure to bright lights 30 minutes before bedtime because it signals the neurons that help control the sleep-wake cycle that it is time to awaken, not to sleep.

Create a sleep-conducive environment that is dark, quiet, comfortable, cool, and free of interruptions. Make your bedroom reflective of the value you place on sleep. Check your room for noise or other distractions, such as your bed partner's snoring, noisy appliances, traffic noise, light, and a dry or excessively hot environment. Consider using blackout curtains, eye shades, ear plugs, white noise, humidifiers, fans, or other sleep devices.

Sleep on a comfortable mattress and pillow. Make sure your mattress is comfortable and supportive. The one you have been using for years may have exceeded its life expectancy, which is about seven or eight years for most good quality mattresses. Use comfortable pillows and make the room attractive and inviting for sleep but also free of allergens that might affect you.

Use your bedroom only for bedroom activities. It is best to take work materials, computers, and televisions out of the sleeping environment. Use your bed only for sleep and sex to strengthen the association between bed and sleep. If you associate a particular activity or item with anxiety about sleeping, eliminate it from your bedtime routine. For example, if looking at a bedroom clock makes you anxious about how much time you have before you must get up, move the clock out of sight.

Limit heavy eating within two hours before your regular bedtime. Eating or drinking too much may make you less comfortable when settling down for bed. It is best to avoid a heavy meal too close to bedtime. Also, spicy foods may cause heartburn, which leads to difficulty falling asleep and discomfort during the night. A small, well-balanced snack before bedtime can help improve the quality of your sleep. It is also best to restrict fluids close to bedtime to prevent nighttime awakenings to go to the bathroom. However, some people find milk or herbal, caffeine-free teas to be soothing and a helpful part of their bedtime routine.

Exercise regularly but avoid intense workouts within two hours before bedtime. Exercising regularly makes it easier to fall asleep and contributes to sounder sleep. However, exercising sporadically or right before going to bed may make falling asleep more difficult. In addition to making you more alert, your body temperature rises during exercise and takes as much as six hours to begin to drop. A cooler body temperature is associated with sleep onset. Finish your exercise at least two hours before bedtime. Late afternoon exercise is the perfect way to help you fall asleep at night.

Avoid caffeine (coffee, tea, soda, chocolate) close to bedtime. Caffeine products remain in the body on average from three to five hours, but they can affect some people up to 12 hours later. Even if you do not think caffeine affects you, it may be disrupting and changing the quality of your sleep. Avoiding caffeine within six to eight hours of going to bed can help improve sleep quality.

Avoid nicotine (cigarettes, tobacco products) close to bedtime. Because nicotine is a stimulant, smoking before bedtime makes it more difficult to fall asleep. You also experience withdrawal symptoms from nicotine, which causes sleep problems. In addition, nicotine can cause problems waking in the morning and may also cause nightmares. Difficulty sleeping is just one more reason to quit smoking.

Avoid alcohol close to bedtime. Although it may help you to fall asleep, alcohol actually alters your sleep patterns and can lead to a less restful sleep. When the alcohol wears off in the middle of the night, your brain thinks it's time to wake up. Alcohol is also a diuretic and the need to urinate may also make you wake up.

Techniques That Will Put You to Sleep

There are many common recommendations for getting better sleep, and we have found the following techniques to work quite well for our clients. Besides improving the quality and quantity of your sleep, they will also help rebalance your ANS.

Progressive Relaxation

Progressive relaxation (originally developed by Edmund Jacobson, PhD) is a highly effective technique to help you relax and fall asleep when you have muscle tension. It works on the theory that opposites can't coexist. Therefore, if you are tense you create more tension until the only option is to completely relax. In progressive relaxation, you tense the muscles starting at the feet and then hold that contraction for a count of 10. At the end of this contraction, your muscles will be tired of being tense, and you will then be able to fully relax them. As you systematically move up from your feet, repeat this contract-and-relax method for all the major muscles in your body. It should be noted that many of our clients never make it through their entire body because they fall asleep before they are finished.

Autogenic Relaxation

Autogenic relaxation (developed by German psychiatrist Johannes Schultz) is a technique to help you relax and fall asleep when you can't turn your mind off. It takes advantage of the fact that your brain wants something to think about so it strategically obliges it. By using autogenic suggestions (verbal cues and images), you focus on one area of the body and then consciously connect your breathing and relaxing thoughts to that area. Autogenic relaxation is also a great technique for relieving pain or tension in a particular part of the body and for encouraging natural healing.

Mental Imagery Techniques

Changing your thoughts before you go to bed is often a necessity in order to help your body relax.

Do you find yourself lying in bed with your mind racing?

Are you thinking of tomorrow and all the tasks that you have to do?

Whether you know it or not, your thoughts are creating the release of a cascade of stress hormones. This not only reduces the quality of your sleep, it also destroys your performance and damages your health.

Performing a mental imagery exercise like envisioning a restful image or place, or focusing on the things you appreciate from your day has been proven to be effective for generating quality sleep. One approach that has been very successful with our clients is mentally visualizing yourself completely relaxed and melting into your bed. Clients who consistently wake up in the middle of the night find that this image (calm and deeply relaxed—the opposite of an image of getting stressed about not being able to sleep) helps them quickly fall back asleep.

This bedtime ritual is a simple but very powerful technique that many of our clients use to let go of their day, positively change their Mindset, turn off their stress response, and improve the quality of their sleep.

Just before you are ready to retire for the evening, lie flat on your bed with your eyes closed. Take three deep, slow breaths in through your nose and out through your relaxed lips. With each breath, focus on your abdomen rising and falling (diaphragmatic breathing) rather than your chest. Feel your lower back expand and sink into your bed with each breath.

Now, go backwards and consciously identify all the things that you appreciate from your day. Examples may include the workout you completed, the hug you got from your son, the time you spent with your daughter reading to her, the way you handled an irate client, your preparations for a strategic meeting, a high performance meal that you ate, or any other event that resonates positively with you. There are no limits to what things, people, and events you may appreciate from your day.

Initially, you may only be able to recall two or three things, but as you practice this ritual, you will remember more and more! The feeling of appreciation has been shown to improve your entire physiology, to relax your body, and to rebalance your ANS.

What if you wake up in the middle of the night and your mind is racing again?

Simply go back to your list of the things you did well during the day and once again, this technique will work like a charm to put you peacefully back to sleep.

Power Naps and Strategic Napping

The human body has innate cycles including 24-hour circadian rhythms. These are crucial for regulating many bodily functions such as hormone levels, body temperature, and metabolic rate. When you take the time to track your own circadian rhythms, you will quickly realize that there are times during the day when you consistently feel tired. There is also a time when your body is telling you to go to sleep. These rhythms are completely normal and during these low circadian rhythms, it is a perfect time to take a power nap.

The US military has studied power naps extensively and their value to increasing alertness and decreasing fatigue. In general, the high performance way to nap is to limit naps to no longer than 30 minutes. Longer naps have been shown to create sleep inertia, which can actually make you feel sluggish and more fatigued for up to an hour after your nap. Power naps of 20 minutes or less reenergize you, and they have virtually no negative impact on your normal nightly sleep cycles.

Naps have also been shown to maintain or improve subsequent performance, physiological and subjective alertness, and mood. In fact, British Airways requires their pilots to take a nap on transoceanic flights to make them more alert for landing.

Nap Times

to quickly shed sleepiness	1 to 5 minutes
to increase performance	5 to 30 minutes
to make up for lost sleep (away from work)	90 + minutes

Note: The 90-minute nap is a good way to diminish sleep deprivation on the weekends. It is a full sleep cycle so it shouldn't cause sleep inertia which could put a damper on the rest of your day.

Napping Enhances Productivity!
An afternoon nap increases productivity by 35 % and decision-making ability by up to 50 %.
Source: NASA

Level 2 – Rebalance and Reenergize

In the second level, we work on rebalancing and reenergizing your brain and body through active Recovery techniques that will give you more energy, passion, focus, and enthusiasm at work and away from work. These strategies include breathing techniques, laughter, and reenergizing movement. The techniques are simple, require little or no planning, and can be done any time throughout your day.

As we noted earlier, we want you to think differently about stress and Recovery. Rather than focusing on stress management, our goal is to help you rebalance your ANS to tap into the natural regenerative processes. It is important to remember that the problem isn't necessarily too much stress; more often, it's the absence of oscillation to allow your body and brain to fully recover.

One of the most natural, efficient, and equipment-free methods to rebalance and reenergize is through focused breathing. Many people never stop to think about their breathing, since their bodies are built to breathe automatically, inhaling a constant source of oxygen and exhaling the waste product carbon dioxide.

If you think that your breathing cannot have an impact on your performance, think again. One of our Tignum clients recently shared: "When I first worked with Tignum, I thought the breathing techniques were a little hokey. But after practicing them now for several months, I'm amazed at what a big impact it has on my recovery and performance."

Take a Deep Breath!

I recently read an article about the power of a strong mindset in race car drivers. At 200 mph (322 kilometers per hour)—just slightly under the current speed of business—the unprepared brain will trigger a panicky jolt of energy that floods the body with adrenalin and cortisol. When this happens, the natural tendency is to hold your breath, which leads to panic, and then all reasonable thinking is shut down.

When Patrick Jacobs worked with Indianapolis 500 winner, Gil de Ferran, he coached him to resist this primal instinct with controlled breathing techniques learned through prana yoga. This approach demonstrates that with practice, breathing can help anyone handle stress, think clearly, and perform her/his best, even under the highest amount of pressure.

If these techniques can be used at 200 mph, they can also be used during a meeting, during a negotiation, or any time that you need sustainable high performance.

Tignum Blog

Breathing Takes Practice

Western scientists have identified that breath is the natural balancer of the ANS. Every inhalation stimulates your sympathetic (fight or flight) nervous system, and every exhalation stimulates your parasympathetic (Recovery) nervous system. Learning to breathe properly can create a mini-recovery break anytime and any place you need it.

In addition, eastern philosophy, for thousands of years, has taught that breath is the connection between the mind and the body. Many cultures have practices that revolve around the incredible power of breath, your life source. There are many different breathing techniques that are used for various benefits and purposes.

When we work with clients, we teach four different techniques and we spend time practicing them to proficiency. For the purposes of this book, we have selected two simple but powerful techniques that are easy to learn and apply, and that will provide maximum benefits. The key to all breathing techniques is practice, practice, practice.

Diaphragmatic Breathing
The flow of inhalation and exhalation provides a natural opportunity for a balance within the ANS. One type of breathing, diaphragmatic breathing, actually stimulates a parasympathetic nerve called the vagus nerve, which starts in the brainstem and conveys sensory information to your central nervous system. The vagus nerve is responsible for a variety of bodily functions such as your heart rate, sweating, contractions for digestion, speech, and muscle movement in your mouth.

To perform diaphragmatic breathing, place your right hand on your chest and your left hand on your abdomen just above your belly button.
First breathe normally and become aware of which hand is doing most of the rising and falling.
Breathe in and out through your nose.
After a minute or so, consciously shift your breathing to keep your right hand (on your chest) almost still while your left hand (on your abdomen) rises and falls with each inhalation and exhalation.
As you practice, close your eyes so you can really focus on breathing fully through your diaphragm.

Diaphragmatic breathing is a simple technique that can be used anytime anywhere to stimulate your parasympathetic nervous system, rebalance your ANS, turn on your right brain (creativity), and reduce the effects of stress. This technique is especially effective in combination with mental imagery.

Ratio Breathing

Since inhalation stimulates your sympathetic (fight or flight) nervous system and exhalation stimulates your parasympathetic (calming and restorative) nervous system, you can vary the response you get by changing the ratio of inhalation to exhalation. By equalizing your inhalation and exhalation in both rate and depth, you can bring your ANS back into balance. This technique is also effective for lowering your heart rate and improving heart rate variability.

To perform ratio breathing, first begin with diaphragmatic breathing, breathing in and out through your nose.

There are many variations to ratio breathing but a good place to start is 4:4 breathing. Simply inhale for a count of four and then exhale for a count of four.

To increase the parasympathetic response (a way to quickly calm yourself), you can shift to a ratio of 4:8. Simply inhale for a count of four and then exhale for a count of eight.

To increase the sympathetic response (a way to increase your energy or focus), you can shift to a ratio of 8:4. Simply inhale for a count of 8 and then exhale for a count of 4. This type of pattern is very common for public speakers who feel they need to psyche themselves up right before they step up to perform.

As you master ratio breathing, you can begin to increase these numbers as long as you maintain the proper ratio for the benefits you want to achieve. This counting is also an excellent way to quiet an overactive mind as you are forced to concentrate on the count of your breathing as you practice your ratios. Experiment with these ratios and become aware of the way they make you feel.

Breathing is a built-in Recovery break that you can take anytime ... while you are in a negotiation, sitting in traffic, on the phone, or after stressful interactions. Take control of your oscillation and breathe for high performance.

"At age 61, odd as it sounds, I have begun to learn to breathe... and it has saved my life and is helping to save (or at least helping me find) my soul. I start the morning with Chi Gong, and take 20-minute breathing meditation breaks twice a day—as well as 'mini-med' breaks hourly. Hey, I even practiced walking breathing-meditation while in the seemingly endless Denver airport security line last week. And, yikes, it worked."
Tom Peters, American Business Consultant and Author

Laugh Your Way to Recovery

It is no joke that laughter improves your state of mind and sense of well-being. And, laughter has also been shown to improve physical health in various ways. For instance, laughter helps relieve stress by releasing endorphins and reducing stress hormones like adrenaline and cortisol. This results in a feeling of a natural high.

Recent studies have shown that laughter is good for your heart, your body, and your immune system. When you laugh, your blood vessels expand, increasing your circulation, ultimately lessening the risk of heart disease. When you laugh, there is also an increase in the cells that kill tumors and viruses, and humor has been show to speed up Recovery from illness and injury.

In addition, when you laugh vigorously out loud, you are forced to breathe more deeply and your oxygen intake increases. This actually produces deep relaxation, as well as an energizing effect.

Humor has also been shown to improve creativity and memory. Learning that is fun or filled with humor is highly effective, and the information associated with humor is more easily retained. Laughter assists in creativity, allowing you to be more open to ideas, more innovative, and more artistic.

Furthermore, current studies on humor in the workplace have demonstrated that laughter also helps in building better relationships with others. In addition to being a tool for social bonding, laughter also aids in communication at the office. In fact, companies that have an atmosphere of humor usually perform better and more consistently. Offices that embrace humor also tend to be more organized and more equipped to handle stressful situations.

In one specific study, Chris Robert, assistant professor in Missouri University's Robert J. Trulaske Sr. College of Business, along with a business doctoral student Wan Yan, found that humor has a meaningful impact on the quality of communication, cohesiveness of relationships, and overall performance in the workplace.

Robert stated, "The ability to appreciate humor, the ability to laugh and make other people laugh actually has physiological effects on the body that cause people to become more bonded."

The Healing Effects of Laughter

I read a recent Japanese study that examined the effect of laughter on diabetes patients. The researchers were measuring the effects of laughter on blood sugar levels and immune cell function. The study intervention was carried out over two days.

The first day, participants were exposed to comic videos and during the laughter, blood samples were taken during three different time periods to measure blood glucose levels and immune cell response. The next day was the control day, and no humor was introduced, but the same blood parameters were measured.

Results revealed that after the period of laughter on the first day, the blood glucose levels over the course of four hours (even with a meal) were better controlled and more steady than the day without laughter. The researchers also reported that on the first day, the increase in natural killer cells suggested that laughter also could have an impact on the immune system. The Japanese doctors that conducted the study concluded that the results add to the growing body of evidence pointing to the healing effects of laughter.

When we work with our clients, we discuss how laughter can offer Recovery and rejuvenation to positively impact performance and sustainability. I always get excited when we can find clinical evidence that is measurable that links the Tignum strategies to performance enhancement and achieving optimal health. By employing laughter as a Recovery tool, you can steady blood sugar and positively impact your immune system—both essential elements for sustainability and peak performance (mentally and physically).

How do you incorporate laughter into your day? I go to YouTube and get my chuckles in with all their humorous video clips.

Tignum Blog

You can also smile to rebalance your ANS. Of the 45 muscles in the face, 40 of them are used to make facial expressions. Researchers have identified over 1,000 facial expressions. These facial expressions provide a window into your thoughts and emotions. Truly, you do wear your emotions on your face.

But can you change your emotions and your physiology by changing your face?

Dr. Paul Ekman, PhD, professor emeritus in the Department of Psychiatry at the University of California Medical School, believes so. Ekman, better known for using facial expressions to determine if a person is telling the truth has been studying the link between facial expressions and emotions for over 32 years. In one of his studies, he had a group of college students make different faces. Then he measured their vital signs including blood pressure and pulse. Sure enough, by simply smiling, participants experienced decreased blood pressure and heart rates. As Ekman notes: "Facial expressions aren't a clue to the mental state; they are the mental state."

Have you ever presented in front of a very intense audience, where you could feel the pressure from their stares, when suddenly you crack a smile and not only did you change, but so did your audience?

How often do you walk around frowning, deep in thought, while your sympathetic nervous system is in fight-or-flight mode? Watch how few people smile as you pass by them. When you become aware of this, you can try smiling at people and saying hello. This is not only great for them, it's great for you.

Every time you smile, you create a Recovery break for yourself. You rebalance your ANS by reducing cortisol and by decreasing your heart rate and your blood pressure.

To download sound-file instructions on breathing and relaxation techniques, go to www.tignum.com/sinkfloatswim and log in with "swimmer."

What are simple Recovery strategies that you can begin using today?

How will you know that your Recovery has improved?

On a scale of 1-10, how committed are you to improving your Recovery?

Chapter Fifteen
Swimming Is A Rhythm

One of the most fundamental principles of exercise is the adaptation principle. In order for people to get stronger or faster, they need to be sure that they overload the muscle and then, just as importantly, they must be sure that the body gets adequate Recovery time. During this Recovery, the muscles not only repair but the repair supercompensates for the overload it received, so the muscles actually get stronger in anticipation of future overloads.

Mentally, you respond exactly the same as you do physically. You need to be pushed, challenged, and stressed, and with adequate Recovery, your mind will improve in its capacity to think, focus, and respond quickly. But if you don't get the Recovery time that you need, you will not improve, and in fact, you will get worse. Even if the stress is minimal, without adequate Recovery, your performance will begin to diminish and eventually you could burn out.

The typical (linear) approach is to think that the harder you work, the greater your performance. While this approach does originally work, it eventually leads to less energy and a weakened immune system. As you keep trying harder and harder, and working longer and longer, your performance eventually plateaus and then it declines. Worse yet, your energy levels decrease and your immune system becomes unable to adequately protect you. This approach is not sustainable.

Level 3 – Strategically Oscillate

This level requires planning to ensure that you oscillate between work and Recovery on a daily, weekly, monthly, and yearly basis. The daily oscillation involves planning strategic breaks during the day where you implement our level two techniques. On a weekly basis, it is critical to have some regeneration time where you can relax, have some fun, and enjoy being "fully off." On a monthly and yearly basis, you should ideally plan vacations where you can allow your mind and body to be fully off for several days in succession. These breaks are vital to your performance and your sustainability.

As the diagram below illustrates, the oscillating approach builds in hard work, along with adequate Recovery. With this approach, performance continues to improve, burnout is prevented, and you are ready for the next challenge. In other words, you become a sustainable high performer—a swimmer.

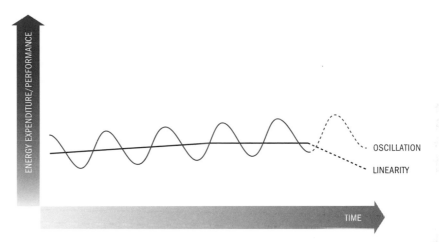

At this point, you should have developed some useful practical strategies for Recovery, to oscillate throughout your day, your week, and your month. The strategies that we've covered thus far such as power naps, breathing techniques, and laughing all provide simple but highly beneficial Recovery and regeneration opportunities in your day.

Ultimately, our goal is to make Performance Recovery through oscillation a strategic-must for you. This means you don't leave it to chance, you don't wait for someone else to plan it for you, and you don't wait until you feel like you're losing it. No, you take the proactive and smart approach—you plan your Recovery.

In addition to the methods we have already presented, there are many other ways to oscillate. These strategies include self-massage, nutritious snacks, and even movement breaks.

How will you plan for your oscillation during your upcoming week, month, or year?

Watch Top Athletes at the Olympics—and Learn!
During the 2008 Olympics, Dara Torres won a silver medal, missing the gold by only .01 of a second. What was her secret to perform at such a high level, at the age of 41, against the best swimmers in the world?
The Dara Torres story really resonates with all of us who have jumped past 40 years old. Torres was the oldest swimmer to medal when she was age 33. But that was already two Olympics ago! Like many of us, she is also a parent (with all the extra demands that come with that), and like many of us, she realizes that she doesn't bounce back like she did at her first international race when she was 14 years old.
After many injuries and setbacks, Torres realized that it wasn't just about how hard or how often she trained. She recognized that it was how well she recovered that really made the difference. The performance strategies that launched Torres onto that medal stand included training only half as much as she did in the past, focusing more on stretching and other restorative modalities, and keeping a mindset that it is the quality of movement that matters most.
In addition, if you watch Torres before and after her races, and in all her interviews, she's always taking advantage of her best relaxation tool—her smile. She is a fantastic role model for sustainable high performers!
Tignum Blog

The Benefits of Relieving Tension

Massage has been around for centuries. Its ability to increase muscle and skin temperature, elicit a relaxation response, decrease resting heart rates and blood pressure, improve mood, and increase the feelings of well-being have been well established. There are many different types of massage (e.g., Swedish, Deep Tissue, Trigger Point, Thai, Hot Stone) and they all offer these benefits. The important thing is for you to find a good masseuse that provides you with the style and pressure that you find regenerating.

In Section IV Performance Movement, we introduced tennis ball massage as a practical way to perform myofascial release on yourself. As we noted, tennis ball massage will reduce muscle tension and pain, and create an opportunity to oscillate. Sitting at your desk, you can take off your shoes and roll the ball under your feet. You can cross your leg and roll the ball over the tight areas on your lateral hips. Or, you can roll the ball on your chest or up and down your neck to prevent headaches or neck pain.

These techniques are easy and effective, but they aren't very common in the workplace. They aren't common because most people don't realize that using a tennis ball can be a quick performance enhancer, especially when they're tense, in pain, or they've been diligently working for hours in one spot.

Use Nutrition for Performance Recovery

Nutrition is a natural Recovery opportunity. Unfortunately, for too many people, eating can become another stressor. This is because they force feed themselves at their desks while they do work, they eat so fast that they forget to swallow (so they can get back to the office), or they eat a meal that is high in sugar, preservatives, or other performance-reducing ingredients.

Skipping lunch is a badge of courage for many executives. It is viewed as proof (so you think) to the rest of the team that you are a performer who is so committed to your work that you have no time to take a lunch break. This is not smart, it is not sustainable, and it is not the behavior of a swimmer.

Eating nutrient dense foods will provide your body with the nutrients necessary to reset your HPA axis and help you avoid the exhaustion phase of the stress response. Similarly, eating slowly, enjoying your food, and taking the time to chew your food thoroughly stimulates the parasympathetic nervous system. Foods rich in tryptophan are excellent for relaxation. These include seafood, whole grains, eggs, dairy, hazelnuts, peanuts, soy products, beans, and hummus. Interestingly enough, these foods are also powerful brain foods. What a high performance way to begin the second half of your day!

Another place where nutrition can be helpful in Recovery is with quality sleep. Bedtime snacks that facilitate better sleep include whole grain cereal with milk (provides calcium and magnesium, as well) or a PBJ (peanut butter and jelly) sandwich. Lighter meals will give you a more restful sleep while high fat and large portions will interfere with your sleep. Chamomile tea is also a natural relaxing herb that is very soothing late at night and an ancient sleep aid.

"Lunch used to be a necessary evil in my day. I would either skip it completely to finish my work or I would rush through it so fast that I couldn't remember what I ate 10 minutes later. When I learned to think of my day as two separate days, both starting with a high performance meal, my thinking really changed. Suddenly lunch became the most important meal of the second half of my day. When I approached this strategically, it doubled my performance for my afternoons.
Now I pack a lunch full of high performance foods and I always leave the office to get a change of scenery. If the weather is nice, I go to the park and I focus on breathing while I chew my food. Then when I'm done I go for a brisk walk for 15 or 20 minutes to help my digestion and to get mentally prepared for my afternoon meetings.
Miraculously, my afternoon dip is gone and my focus, concentration, and energy level has improved so much. This small shift in my thinking has really helped."
Tignum Client

Incorporate Movement for Performance Recovery

Movement is another excellent tool for Recovery. Full body movements can be very restorative. The increase in circulation, improvement in mobility, neuro-stimulation, and metabolism of stress hormones are all essential to achieving Recovery. The Tignum Daily Prep exercises, climbing a few flights of stairs, or simply going for a walk are all effective Movement strategies to enhance Recovery.

There are many benefits of going for a walk when you are feeling stressed. A walk provides more than a change in scenery; it also improves the blood flow to the brain and stimulates the right brain. It may be difficult to believe that something as simple as a walk can be so powerful, but think about when you had your last breakthrough moment. Was it sitting at your desk? In a highly stressful meeting? Or was it while you were taking a walk or during some other Recovery break?

Another simple way to improve your Recovery is to incorporate static stretches into your daily routine. These stretches are less active than our Daily Prep exercises, but they work well for reducing tension and lengthening muscles back to their relaxed state.

The key is not to leave these opportunities for Recovery to chance. Plan them into your day, week, and month. Use them strategically to oscillate for high performance.

Do you oscillate or do you wait until you are exhausted?

Evaluate Your Recovery Habits

The more you increase your awareness and practice the Performance Recovery strategies we have presented, the better your performance will be. Many of these strategies require minimal time and doing them consistently will yield amazing results. Incorporate them into your workday whether you are at the office or traveling, if you want to work smart rather than hard.

Too often people leave their Recovery to chance. One of our clients declared: "If you want to know what's important to people, just look at their daily calendars." Today is the best day for you to schedule some Performance Recovery. Better yet, look at your week and your month to see where your tough days are. Where does it look like your workload is too linear? Where can you add some oscillation?

Note that our Recovery approach is not necessarily focused on working less. We can appreciate the fact that many of our clients love to work. They love their jobs, they're committed to getting everything done, and they really find joy in what they can accomplish at work. If you fit into this category, we say that it will only be through oscillation that you will be able to remain a high performer. With the work smart approach, rather than the work hard approach, you will actually be able to work longer, be more efficient, and produce better results. Although you may not take many days off of work, you can, and must, take several Performance Recovery breaks throughout your day.

Do you want to sink, float, or swim?

The choice is always yours.

You have Recovery habits that will make you **sink** if you:

_are unaware of where your stress comes from or where you feel it in your body
_spend little or no time reflecting on how you feel and what makes you feel good
_ignore the signs that you are becoming overwhelmed
_have no conscious or planned daily Recovery time because you perceive
  recovery breaks as a sign of weakness
_rarely laugh or smile
_rarely take power naps even if you are tired because you see them as a
  sign of laziness
_sleep less than seven hours on most nights and do not go to sleep at
  a consistent time
_go to sleep after 10:30 pm on most nights and often do work in your bedroom
_have no ritual or routine to wind down before going to sleep
_rely on medication to sleep when under you're under stress or traveling
_do not plan for fun time in your day, week, month, or year
_rarely take vacation days and work on almost all of your days off
_never implement any relaxation techniques even when you feel extremely tense
_are unaware of your breathing patterns and their impact on your autonomic
  nervous system
_are unaware of the role of relaxation and Recovery on your brain performance
_are unaware that Mindset, Nutrition, Movement, and Recovery impact your
  energy, resilience, brain performance, and capacity

You have Recovery habits that will enable you to **float** if you:

_are aware of where your stress comes from and where you feel stress in your
  body, but don't really address it
_try to take regular Recovery breaks but you don't strategically plan for them
_laugh or smile occasionally, but it is not a regular occurrence
_occasionally take power naps but only if you are extremely tired
_generally sleep seven hours on most nights but are inconsistent with the
  time you go to bed
_go to sleep after 10:30 pm at least two or three nights a week, and occasion-
  ally do work in your bedroom
_have a routine to wind down before going to sleep but don't use it consistently
_occasionally plan for fun time in your day, week, month, or year
_occasionally take vacation days but you feel guilty for missing work,
  and usually work on some of your time off
_implement relaxation techniques but only when you feel extremely tense
_are aware of your breathing patterns and their impact on your autonomic
  nervous system but only use breathing techniques occasionally to help you
  reduce stress and tension
_use a relaxation technique to focus before a must-win presentation or
  meeting, but not consistently
_are somewhat aware of the role of relaxation and Recovery strategies on your
  brain performance, but do not integrate them with Mindset, Nutrition, and
  Movement strategies

You have Recovery habits to **swim** if you:

_are aware of where your stress comes from and proactively manage it to avoid becoming overwhelmed

_frequently reflect on how you feel and what makes you feel good

_consciously plan Recovery time for every day because you recognize this as a sign of strength and working smart

_often find things to make you laugh or smile each day

_take power naps if you are tired during the day since you recognize their importance as a tool for sustainable high performance

_sleep close to eight or nine hours on most nights and go to sleep at the same time almost every night

_rarely go to sleep after 10:30 pm and never do work in your bedroom

_have a ritual or routine to wind down before going to sleep and habitually use it

_plan for fun time in your day, week, month, or year

_take your vacation days and use them for fun and regenerating activities, and rarely, if ever, work on your time off

_implement relaxation techniques when you feel any sign of tension

_are aware of your breathing patterns and their impact on your autonomic nervous system and frequently use them to help you reduce your stress and tension

_use a relaxation technique to focus before almost all of your presentations or must-win events

_are aware of the role of relaxation and Recovery on your brain performance and strategically use it to improve your creativity, passion, and focus

_effectively integrate your Performance Mindset, Performance Nutrition, and Performance Movement habits with your Performance Recovery strategies

Develop Your Performance Recovery Goals

The sustainable High Performance Recovery strategies presented in this chapter are designed to be integrated with our Performance Mindset, Performance Nutrition, and Performance Movement strategies. These Recovery strategies alone will not necessarily make you a high performer or increase the sustainability of your performance. In fact, it is very unlikely that you can have High Performance Recovery if you are hypoglycemic, malnourished, or sedentary. The four Tignum pillars of sustainable high performance are intricately interwoven and dependent upon each other. The true power of personal innovation comes with the integration of Mindset, Nutrition, Movement, and Recovery habits.

In order to take everything you have learned and create High Performance Recovery, you need to develop Recovery goals that are meaningful to you. To begin this process, consider the following questions:

What three action steps can you take now to help you improve your Recovery?

If you were to have a High Performance Recovery day, what will your day look like?

How will you know when you need a Recovery break?

What are the benefits of moving from a linear approach to oscillating for Recovery?

How will you use Performance Recovery strategies to help you increase your energy, resilience, brain performance, and capacity for sustainable high performance?

Section VI
Swimming Into the Future

High Performance Culture – an environment in which leaders foster a passion for creativity, productivity, and the achievement of individual, team, organization, and brand potential

Chapter Sixteen
If You Know You Need to Swim, Why Aren't You Doing It?

Chapter Seventeen
Does Your Team Have What It Takes to Swim?

Chapter Eighteen
Is Your Organization Sinking, Floating, or Swimming?

Chapter Nineteen
Time to Dive In

Chapter Sixteen
If You Know You Need to Swim, Why Aren't You Doing It?

Have you ever tried to make a personal change and failed? Have you ever attended a training course or leadership program, been thoroughly impressed and motivated, but then failed to make any sustainable changes? It happens all the time. In fact, when we work with our clients, their initial apprehension is commonly rooted in their frustration from previous attempts (and failures) to make real changes in their lives. What is the disconnect here? Why does this happen so often? The answers to these questions haunted us when we first began Tignum, because we were firmly committed to making an impact, which translated into making real change.

There is a commonly accepted belief that people don't change because they do not know WHAT to do. In our opinion, the reason most people don't change is because they do not have a deeply meaningful reason WHY they should change. There are often many different HOWs or ways to change but without the WHY, change won't happen.

Nothing motivates real change like facing a crisis. True or false?

Unfortunately, this is a myth. In a Fast Company article entitled "Change or Die," published in May 2005, author Alan Deutschman shared a staggering statistic. In the US, only two years after suffering a heart attack and receiving a coronary bypass, 90% of the 600,000 bypass patients did not change their lifestyles. This means even the risk of another heart attack, another heart surgery, or even worse—death—is not enough of a motivator for the majority of people to make a change in their lives.

People don't embrace change because it's the right thing to do or because they are logically convinced to make the change. People change because of the benefits associated with the change. Simply stated, they change for the emotional payback, the feelings that come with making the change.

What kinds of things motivate you to change?

Why have you made changes in the past?

How did you feel after making a significant change?

What's Wrong With Goals?

In business, there is a preponderance of goal setting, which is perceived as crucial for measuring results and creating accountability. The type of goals most commonly used are SMART goals. (SMART stands for Specific, Measurable, Attainable, Realistic, and Time-based goals.) These types of goals are very concise, tangible, and logical. Unfortunately, they lack one very significant element that is necessary for real and lasting change, and that is the emotion.

We have observed that one of the biggest factors in our clients' success is developing emotional and meaningful goals. If a goal has no meaning and doesn't touch an emotional chord, then the chances of achieving it are very unlikely. Similarly, when you look at many positive-thinking programs, they stress to-have goals. These include lofty goals of making millions of dollars, having a beach villa, driving the latest high performance car, or living in a dream home. The thought is that these tangible items, which may appear to be just out of reach, will provide an emotional connection to change behavior.

The problem with this approach is that these goals focus on extrinsic motivation, which research has shown to be a weak and short-term motivator. People don't change because of a plan or goals—they change because of an emotional connection. They change because of the feeling that the achievement of the goal will evoke. This doesn't mean that SMART goals are necessarily bad or ineffective. It only means that they often are not enough.

At Tignum, we see four common flaws when people develop their goal and objective statements. They set goals that:

_they have no burning desire to achieve
_are imprecise and difficult to visualize
_do not match their self-image
_are outcome-oriented rather than performance-oriented

Compelling Goals Move You to Action

First of all, goals must be personally meaningful. In most cases, people will not be motivated to meet goals that have come from a boss or someone else, or if they have been motivated by social expectations. We always ask our clients why they want to accomplish a certain goal that they've identified. They are often not able to articulate a specific (or meaningful) reason. Their answers sound like this: My doctor told me I should lose weight or my boss says I need to be more solution-oriented. As soon as we hear statements like these, we challenge them to find the specific reason for why they want to accomplish the goal.

So, the first step to developing goals that will move you to action is to ask:

Why is accomplishing this goal important to YOU?

If you can't find a meaningful answer this question, you either need to dig deeper to find personal meaning or change the goal. Finding this meaning will give your goal the emotion necessary to move you to action.

Second, in order for a goal to be achieved, people must be able to visualize themselves achieving it. Too often we see clients set great goals, but they are completely outside of their scope of experiences. Unfortunately, once a habit is developed, most people struggle immensely to envision themselves behaving differently. Being able to envision yourself achieving your goals is critical to realizing them. Changing your mental map is the initial step to real change.

For example, we worked with a client who was a true junk food addict. He couldn't go to a meeting or have a meal without a piece of cake, some candy, or some low nutrient/high calorie food. He knew that these food choices were contributing to his decreased energy in the afternoons, as well as his lack of attention and focus in meetings. So, logically, the reason for making a change made sense. He wanted to improve his performance in meetings, especially after lunch. He was motivated to change this behavior, but he kept sliding back to his old habit.

With some work, we helped him create a clear vision of himself changing this behavior. He started to see himself making different choices and experiencing the benefits. He saw himself as a highly attentive, focused contributor at his after-noon meetings. Within three weeks (with lots of repetition of mentally rehearsing this positive image), he completely changed his behavior.

Third, matching the goal to self-image (goal congruency) is crucial to bridging the gap between where people are now and where they want to be in the future. In our experience, most people can use work on their self-image, and this is why developing **To Be** goals is vital to making change.

It's one thing to be able to visualize yourself achieving a goal but it's another thing to believe that you will achieve it. The Tignum Benefit Attainment system, with practical tools like our Personal Innovation Map, is designed with the steps and the reps (repetitions of high performance habits) to build this belief.

Lastly, while outcome goals may seem logical, they can become pressure traps because the outcomes are often out of people's control. Performance-oriented goals, on the other hand, are within their circle of control and when accomplished can help develop self-esteem and self-confidence. Following are some examples of performance goals:

_I will use mental imagery to prepare for every meeting that I have this week.
_I will only drink water at meetings.
_I will do Daily Prep movements five times this week.
_I will take a short Recovery break every 90 minutes during my workday.

Performance goals are usually tangible, narrower in focus, and easy to accomplish. They are often underrated because of this, but when they are done consistently, they lead to significant results. In addition, the momentum that is created from habitually performing the actions you identified will pay huge dividends as you move forward.

The Tignum Benefit Attainment Process

We believe that all people have the inherent ability to solve their own problems especially if they are given the correct tools, encouraged to use their strengths, and supported along the way. We believe that intrinsic, rather than extrinsic, motivation is the key. People are only going to change if it will make them feel fulfilled and allow them to reach their potential. That is how and why we have developed our Benefit Attainment Process.

Why do we call it benefit attainment rather than change management?

The term "change management" has deep roots in organizational change initiatives and often elicits a sense of apprehension. Many of our clients have shared with us that just the word "change" can create resistance. We have found, that especially in the business world, the phrase change management often evokes a vision of getting on the change treadmill and mucking through yet another set of check-off lists.

But when you approach it differently—you reframe change to be focused on the benefits—you have the potential to make meaningful and lasting change. While animals are often trained through avoidance of pain and discomfort, human beings are more motivated by benefits. This is evident by the amount of pain that many people will endure to achieve something they really want. In our opinion, people don't fail to change because they think it will be uncomfortable. They usually fail to change because they either were not focused on the benefits or they never really found the benefits from the change very meaningful.

Look at the amount of pain and discomfort that Olympic athletes will endure for years on end, because they are focused on the feelings and benefits they will attain if they win a medal. This is the big difference between sustainable high performers (swimmers), in both business and sports, and those who continue to float or even sink. Swimmers stay focused on the benefits and see every sacrifice and setback as a part of achieving those benefits.

Make Lasting Change

John Kotter, Harvard Business School Professor and leading authority on leadership and change, notes: "Behavior change happens mostly by speaking to people's feelings. This is true even in organizations that are very focused on analysis and quantitative measurement." In other words, making change is all about your emotional connection to that change.

A very effective way to create an emotional connection is to develop a clear and compelling image of who you want to be in the future (**To Be** goals). This is different from what you want to do, what you want to have, or similar types of goals. The vision of your best self has less to do with your current job or role and more to do with the qualities and attributes you want to have. It also has to do with the legacy you want to leave and the way you want people to feel when they are around you.

Developing a vision of your best self is not always easy to do. It requires getting past the image that you currently have of yourself. This image can sometimes be self-defeating, because it is based on your frailties and limitations. The following example is one of our client's articulated visions of best self:

"I see myself waking up and immediately starting my day. I do some movement and then quickly review my daily schedule and prepare my mindset. Throughout the day, I am focused and attentive in every conversation I have. I can see the connection I am making with my team. I am patient and totally in control of my emotions. I am proactive rather than reactive. I have good posture and I exude confidence. I see myself constantly oscillating, moving from one high performance event to the next. On the way home, I am relaxed and I leave my work and worries at the office. At home, I see myself smiling and excited while my daughter shares the details of her day. I see myself engaged with my wife and excited to share my day and hear about her day. I am patient and totally nonjudgmental."

Amazingly, we have found that once our clients develop a detailed and explicit vision of their best self, they often begin to see their thoughts, behaviors, and habits change almost simultaneously. In addition, they have a clear image with which to compare their current actions.

Some daily questions to ask yourself when you are making a personal change include:

Did I do the necessary things today to create my best self?

If not, how can I change my behaviors tomorrow to achieve my goal?

The career path of Andre Agassi provides an excellent illustration of the use of **To Be** goals. Throughout tennis history, Agassi had many peaks and setbacks in his career. One of his worst setbacks was in 1993 when he had wrist surgery and his world ranking plummeted. During his recovery time, Agassi developed the vision of his best self, as he recognized and defined the legacy he wanted to leave on the game of tennis. This vision became his driving force when he went back into the trenches of competition. He committed to a new set of habits and rituals that not only changed him forever, but also left a lasting legacy on the tennis world.

Upon retiring from professional tennis, when Agassi gave his final farewell speech, he didn't mention how many tournaments or championships he had won. Instead, he spoke about the journey he had taken, the relationships he had experienced with his fans and competitors, and the man it had made him. He talked about the benefits he had personally received from the hard work and sacrifices he had made. There wasn't a dry eye in the stadium, because everyone was moved by the person that Agassi had become.

After leaving the stadium, Agassi walked into the players' locker room and was greeted with a standing ovation by all the players and sports writers. It was an experience that one sports writer said he had never witnessed before. This was impact, and this represented the legacy Agassi had left not only on tennis, but on the world. This is the power of deeply meaningful **To Be** goals.

Power of the To Be Goal

Occasionally, I have clients who are going through a life challenge or a true crisis. Perhaps they have an impossible job, they have to live away from their family, or they are going through a divorce, a serious illness, or even a death in their family. During these times, I always remind my clients that these situations are temporary, but the opportunities they offer for true transformation could last forever.

*These types of events can really exhaust you, throw you off your course, or take away your passion for work or life. They can be real performance busters. But the reality is that discomfort, and even pain, is a great teacher if you take the time to reflect on the lessons it can teach you. The key, though, is to always have a **To Be** goal.*

Who do you want to be when this crisis is over?

What are the benefits of you becoming this person?

Can you envision yourself being this person?

If you focus on the answers to these questions, you will suddenly find the discomfort and pain bearable—because the new you will be worth the effort.

Tignum Blog

The Benefits of Being Your Best

After developing a precise **To Be** (best self) vision, the next step is to identify the benefits of making it a reality. As we stated earlier, benefits are critical to increasing drive and motivation, and ultimately achieving your potential. External benefits such as getting more pay, a promotion, or an award tend to be short-lived but effective for providing initial motivation. Internal benefits such as a feeling of achievement, being respected, feeling loved, and connecting with others provide more long-term motivation and real meaning.

When we work with our clients, we use several techniques to help them discover their meaningful benefits for embarking on their personal innovation journey. There are many ways to brainstorm and develop a list of benefits, but one very popular approach is to create mind maps. Mind mapping has been used for centuries by educators, engineers, psychologists, and others for brainstorming, learning, and problem-solving.

Mind maps are an excellent visual tool to develop a comprehensive list of deeper ideas and thoughts. By focusing on benefits, you can brainstorm all the ways that your **To Be** vision will benefit you, grouping your reasons in a nonlinear way and drawing connections as you make them.

Initially, many of our clients struggle with uncovering meaningful benefits of achieving their **To Be** goals, but we always push them to keep digging. Every time they come up with a benefit we ask them—why? This helps them take it one level deeper. In our experience, virtually no one really discovers meaningful benefits on their first attempt. This is an exercise that takes some genuine exploration and deep reflection.

The point to remember:

The more meaningful the benefit, the more powerful it will be to help you achieve real and lasting change.

Develop and Activate Your Support System

Some people love to work alone while others love to work in groups. The same is true when it comes to personal change, but after working with thousands of executives, we have definitely found that all people need someone to support their efforts in achieving their personal innovation. One critical component in effectively handling setbacks and difficult times is a strong support system. Thus, the next step to achieving your **To Be** goals is to develop your support system. This support can be found through mentors, friends, family, co-workers, or even role models you may not know personally.

In fact, our clients often have role models, people whom they have never personally met but whom they admire. They may see many of the same qualities and attributes that they want to achieve in these people. We encourage you to include these people as part of your support system, since you can reflect on what they would offer for advice if you were to speak with them.

In our work, we have also found that members within a team often support each other and build some of the deepest and most meaningful bonds they have ever experienced. This makes complete sense to us, because what could be a more authentic team-building experience than helping a colleague achieve her/his personal **To Be** vision?

There are many ways to use your support system and they vary considerably from one person to the next. However, one thing that does seem to consistently help our clients is sharing their Personal Innovation Map with their support system. This builds in an element of accountability and enables your support system to provide you with the encouragement you may need to remain on track.

Use Setbacks to Refocus, Recommit, and Ignite Motivation

One lesson we have learned from working with our clients, is that the path to developing new high performance habits (or any change for that matter) is never linear. There will definitely be setbacks. At first glance, these setbacks can appear to be moments of failure. They can appear to be proof to yourself that you don't have the discipline or the commitment to really change, but nothing could be further from the truth.

Failure Feeds Success
There are always a few people who comment that this time they don't want to fail like they have in previous attempts to change. I love this comment because it demonstrates their commitment, but it also shows their fear of falling into the same traps they have experienced before. At Tignum, we realize that changing habits is never easy. We also realize that every change has mini-setbacks (or dips).

For some clients, their previous failures have been so prevalent or emotional that they truly can't see themselves being successful. Instead, the only image they have is being initially excited and motivated, and then looking at themselves in the mirror one day and asking what happened. This is totally normal because that's the way the brain works.

But, it doesn't have to be this way.

In fact, research has shown that one of the best indicators of future success in developing new habits may be how many times you've previously failed. This is because each time you try to change yourself, you learn something new about yourself, you become more motivated, and you get closer to success. Therefore, a quick reframe of previous failures is to see them as practice sessions for making the real change.

And, as we affirm again and again—you are only one day away from being right on track!

Tignum Blog

Seth Godin, in his book The Dip: A Little Book That Teaches You When to Quit, clearly identifies the dips in a change process as expected and necessary for exceptional performance. In fact, he identifies several reasons that people may fail to make a change:

"You

_run out of time (and quit)

_run out of money (and quit)

_get scared (and quit)

_are not serious about it (and quit)

_lose interest or enthusiasm (take your eye off of your vision) or settle for being mediocre (and quit)

_focus on the short-term instead of the long-term (and quit when the short-term gets too hard)"

As you can deduce, the common element here for all of these failures is quitting. But remember, quitting is a choice. Sometimes it can mean that the benefit you were chasing wasn't that important to you, but many times quitting is the wrong choice. The truth is that almost everything in life worth doing is controlled by the dip. The dip is the long slump between starting something new and mastering it. It's the long stretch between beginner's luck and real accomplishment.

The reality is that setbacks are actually an opportunity for change, and it's really all about how you perceive and respond to these setbacks. Successful people don't just ride out their dips. They don't just buckle down and survive. No, they lean into it. They see each setback as an opportunity to push harder, to change the rules, to develop better skills, and to win at all odds. The confidence that comes from this approach is remarkable and so is the momentum and experience. This doesn't mean that you enjoy the dip. It just means that you don't quit—you do everything that you can to whittle it down. We have found that our clients who have learned to push on and conquer their setbacks have always become more confident, more impactful, and better performers because of it.

It is vital to always remember that personal, and organizational, sustainable performance is an ongoing work in progress. This is completely normal since no one can be on the top of her/his game at all times. The nature of change and of improvement is that you make progress, you have small setbacks, you reinspire yourself (by revisiting your benefits and best vision of self), and then you get back to your new habits.

Another common path on the journey of personal innovation is the misconception that with any setback you are right back where you started. You begin your benefit attainment process and two months later, you feel like you have come full circle. You're struggling with the same things that you were struggling with before. This can be demoralizing because you thought you were past this struggle. You thought you were on to a bigger and better struggle or challenge.

The truth is that you are never back at the same place you started. You are more aware, smarter, more experienced, and better prepared to tackle this challenge the next time. It's like an upward spiral. You have come full circle but you're at a higher place in the spiral. You're looking at the same issue from a different angle, and you should feel good about this.

A Crisis Is the Perfect Time to Redefine Success

I just got off the phone with one of our clients. She was very frustrated because no matter what she does she can't close a deal. Being a highly successful sales VP for a very big software company, this type of resistance is something she has never experienced before. We discussed her Mindset and the challenges she is facing with trying to reframe her frustrations and rejections to make her thoughts and self talk more high performance and positive.

As we talked, I recognized that one thing that has shifted in these tough times is the definition of success. If you are married to your quarterly projections, your gross income, or your net profits, you are clearly set up for failure. The solution, not just during this crisis but all the time, is to become more process-oriented in your goals. That is, focus on the processes that you know lead to success.

Recently, Geoff Colvin, in his enlightening book Talent is Overrated: What Really Separates World-Class Performers From Everybody Else, presents some compelling research on goal setting and success. The poorest performers don't set any goals at all. Mediocre performers set goals that are general and often focused simply on achieving a good outcome. But the best performers set goals that are not about outcomes, but rather about the processes of reaching the outcomes.

So the big question is: What are these processes?

These processes are the ones that increase your energy level, your resilience, your brain performance, and your capacity. If you let these processes go, you don't have a chance of being a sustainable high performer or surviving these tough times. Once you commit to the processes necessary for your Performance Mindset, Performance Nutrition, Performance Movement, and Performance Recovery habits, you will quickly enjoy the benefits of being more passionate, confident, focused, and creative. With these qualities, you will be ready to get back to your fundamentals and plant all the seeds that will lead to future success.

Tignum Blog

You also need to recognize your small victories in redefining the meaning of success.

Many times, clients believe that they haven't made any changes because they have often been too busy or stressed out to notice them. But upon further reflection, they realize that they are drinking more water, snacking on high performance foods, preparing mentally for meetings, having more positive thoughts, taking short walks for Recovery, and climbing the stairs (sometimes many flights) every day.

This revelation hits them almost immediately—they actually have made many changes. But since they are so aware now of what they are not doing, they temporarily lost their focus. Once they regain their positive focus, they realize that they are handling more, working smarter, getting more done; and it's all due to the small, daily improvements they have already made.

Maximize Motivation and Build Momentum

Sir Isaac Newton's First Law of Motion states that an object at rest tends to stay at rest and an object in motion tends to stay in motion. Once people begin to make personal changes to improve their energy, resilience, brain performance, and capacity, it is important to keep the motivation going and build momentum. Below are some examples of strategies that our clients have successfully used to do this.

This list is not necessarily comprehensive, so don't feel like you have to limit yourself to these suggestions. Develop your own list of personalized strategies because everyone is different, and only you can determine what will be effective for you.

Develop Social Networks. Change is contagious and developing a social network of people who are going through the same process can help keep your motivation strong.

Create Anchors. Having a word, an object, a song, a photo, or some other item that immediately reminds you of the changes you want to make can be an effective tool for reenergizing your commitment to change.

Use Rituals. Anything done consistently rewires the brain and creates an exponential impact. Rituals such as drinking a glass of water upon getting up, doing your Daily Prep in the mornings, doing mental imagery before meetings, or taking a few rhythmic breaths every time you hang up the phone can help you stay on track.

Send Yourself Reminders. Life happens and sometimes you just need a reminder about what you are trying to achieve. Adding reminders to team meetings, having an alarm in your phone to remind you to take a break, or having your assistant remind you to pack high performance snacks for a business trip can be excellent ways to keep you on track.

Take the Challenge. Just as some of you will love a social network, some of you will love a good challenge. Creating challenges with yourself, your support system, or your team members can be a productive way to keep you performing your best. One note: challenges around effort and action (e.g., performing your movements three days consistently) are usually more powerful than challenges focused on outcomes (e.g., how fast you run or how many pounds you lose).

The Tignum Benefit Attainment Process
In order to help you to move from knowing to doing, we have developed a process that will systematically help you achieve the personal innovation that you desire.
Go to www.tignum.com/sinkfloatswim and login with the password "swimmer" to download a template for your Personal Innovation Map.

At this point, you may have already identified several changes that you would like to make. Consider the following:

What three actions can you start tomorrow?

What will be the benefits of making these small changes?

How will you measure your success?

Chapter Seventeen
Does Your Team Have What It Takes to Swim?

"If you want to go fast, go alone. If you want to go far, go together."
African Proverb

Cisco's CEO John Chambers is heralded as a role model in the use of collaboration to improve productivity, efficiency, and profitability. In a 2008 Fast Company article, "How Cisco's CEO John Chambers is Turning the Tech Giant Socialist," author Ellen McGirt explains that Chamber's goal "... is to spread the company's leadership and decision making far wider than any big company has attempted before, to working groups that currently involve 500 executives. This move, Chambers says, reflects a new philosophy about how business can best work in a networked world."

Chambers is implementing this change because he recognizes that this is the only way to rapidly respond to clients' needs in the dynamic Web 2.0 world. This is an evolving world full of teleconferences, web meetings, blogging, vlogging, and social networking.

To some, this online collaboration may appear to be a world of chaos. To others, it will be a world full of opportunities and possibilities. When collaboration is the norm, the team effectiveness and efficiency will hinge on every member being a contributor. It will depend on a high level of trust and a commitment by every person to be a sustainable high performer. This commitment will require a team approach to Performance Mindset, Performance Nutrition, Performance Movement, and Performance Recovery habits.

In business everything is built on high performance teams. It may be a finance team, a leadership team, a project team, or even a team put together to handle a current crisis. In the previous chapters, we discussed the importance of leaders' ability to first energize themselves so that they could then energize those around them. Creating teams with the energy, focus, resiliency, and capacity to win their battles cannot be left to chance. Like personal sustainable high performance, team or organizational high performance is a choice that must be made.

When you look around your organization, surely you can identify teams that are sinking, teams that may be floating along, and those rare high performance teams that are swimming. Imagine being part of a team where every single person has a High Performance Mindset, is nourished through Nutrition to have a high performing brain, is energized and pain free through regular Movement, and is fully rested and regenerated through consistent Recovery habits.

What would your meetings be like with a high performance team?

How would you feel during and after those meetings?

Team Performance Mindset

Is a Mindset contagious? This is a question we always ask our clients. At first, the reaction is interesting because people look at us like we're trying to give them a virus. But after a little thought, the answer is always a resounding "yes." There are numerous stories about how Michael Jordon transformed the Chicago Bulls with his positive attitude and his relentless commitment to excellence. Similarly, in his autobiography Winning!: The Story of England's Rise to Rugby World Cup Glory, Clive Woodward tells story after story of how he planted Mindset seeds to turn the England National Rugby team around to win the 2003 World Cup.

Anne Mulcahy, CEO of Xerox and one of America's most influential leaders, provides one of the best examples of how contagious a Mindset can be. After taking over the company in the middle of a financial meltdown, she led a legendary turnaround by infusing both the customer base and the company culture with her optimism, pragmatism, and passion for Xerox. Her Mindset helped transform the company, and her unbending focus on clients' needs, rather than on financial engineering, is a preeminent example of innovation used in many business schools.

Whether it's an athletic team, a project team, a leadership team, or any other type of team, most people do believe that a Mindset is contagious. If one team member, especially if it's the leader, has confidence, optimism, or simply a positive attitude, everyone on the team is positively impacted. Similarly, if a team member is pessimistic, problem-oriented (rather than solution-oriented), angry, and negative, the entire team is negatively impacted.

What is your team's Mindset like?

Does your Mindset improve or diminish the team's Mindset?

What could you personally do to improve your team's Mindset?

In discussions with our clients, we ask them to share how they would implement the Tignum Mindset strategies within their team and their organization. Following are some solutions that they have identified to develop a team or organizational Performance Mindset:

_Develop a description of what you want your team Mindset to be like.
_Challenge each other (in a supportive and positive way) to eliminate attitudes and actions that bring the team's Mindset down.
_Encourage each other to mentally prepare for your must-win events.
_Provide useful and frequent feedback to each other to help everyone improve.
_Use the paper-clip exercise during your team meetings to encourage everyone to reframe negative low performance thoughts into positive high performance thoughts.
_Review your past performances, focusing on what you did well so that you can repeat it.

How can you incorporate some of these Mindset strategies in your team?

How about in your organization?

Team Performance Nutrition

As you learned in the Nutrition chapters of this book, what you eat significantly impacts your energy, resilience, brain performance, and capacity. Most importantly, you now recognize that the food you eat directly impacts your performance and your team's performance. So, with this in mind, consider the following:

Who plans the food choices for your meetings?

Who determines the food choices in your vending machines or office kitchen?

How can you work with your food vendor or canteen to offer better choices?

Do you provide water during meetings or do you serve only hydration-robbers?

In discussions with our clients, we ask them to share how they would implement the Tignum Nutrition strategies within their team and their organization. Following are some solutions that they have identified to develop a team or organizational Performance Nutrition approach:

_Provide high performance snacks in vending machines and the office kitchen.
_Get one-liter water bottles for all of the team members and encourage them to drink one full bottle in the morning and another one in the afternoon.
_Provide high performance snacks such as nuts, dried fruit, fresh fruit, yogurt, and energy bars to positively impact brain performance.
_Plan nutrition for all meetings—in weekly, brainstorming, off-site, and strategy meetings.
_Educate all staff about high performance requirements for meetings.
_Create a list of vendors that will follow Tignum high performance recommendations to cater meetings and events.
_Select restaurants for business dinners and team meetings that have high performance menu options.

How can you incorporate some of these Nutrition strategies in your team?

How about in your organization?

Team Performance Movement

It often amazes us how seldom people move during their day. They take the elevator up one flight of stairs or even more commonly, they send colleagues an e-mail or an instant message rather than walking down the hall or up the stairs to talk with them in person. Unfortunately, in many organizations, the stairwells are cold, dark, and difficult to find (even in the case of an emergency). Although this may be an excuse for taking the elevator, it isn't the best choice if you want to become a swimmer.

If you were to take the stairs (rather than the elevator) three floors each day, you would save approximately 5,000 watt/hours of electricity a year. This doesn't seem like a huge savings, but multiply this by the number or people in your organization and the number of high-rises in your city. The savings add up quickly.

Furthermore, the average person will burn approximately 10 calories for every minute s/he climbs the stairs. If you assume a minimum of 10 minutes per workday, this would mean 500 additional calories per week which is approximately 24,000 calories per year. This is the equivalent of 7 pounds (3.18 kilograms) of weight loss each year.

At the Mayo Clinic, endocrinologist James Levine, MD, PhD, performed a study in 2007 to evaluate the impact of the elimination of chairs and traditional desk seating in order to encourage walking. Walking tracks were installed with electronic smart boards strategically placed to capture notes. In addition, desks were attached to treadmills to create walking workstations.

During the six-month study, the participants averaged almost nine pounds (4.1 kilograms) of weight loss. "Another key finding—no productivity was lost due to the new environment. In fact, company officials say revenue rose nearly 10 percent during the first three months of the study, and the company recorded its highest-ever monthly revenue in January 2008—the study's midpoint."

Imagine taking a five-minute movement break every morning and afternoon to walk the stairs. Talk about win-win solutions. What if your entire team participated? Talk about energy! As we say at Tignum—if you're on top of things, why take the elevator?

In discussions with our clients, we ask our clients to brainstorm how they would implement the Tignum Movement strategies within their team and their organization. Following are some solutions that they have identified to develop a team or organizational Performance Movement approach:

_Encourage the use of the stairs (rather than the elevator) as often as possible.
_Utilize the stairwells, making them a fun and exciting place to go.
_Encourage standing meetings.
_Have walking meetings. (This solves the long meeting dilemma, too.)
_Have the team prepare for meetings with a group two-minute movement session. You can also repeat this activity after each break.
_Set up scheduled daily movement sessions for Daily Prep in the mornings.

How can you incorporate some of these Movement strategies in your team?

How about in your organization?

Team Performance Recovery

In bicycle racing, the leading riders form a peloton, which is a pack of riders who break away from the larger group and ride very closely together. They don't ride together because they like each other or because they need a social break. They form the peloton to increase their efficiency in pulling away from the pack. They do this by drafting off of each other, which makes the whole group faster. When they do this, each rider takes a turn pulling at the front of the pack for a short distance and then rotating to the rear to rest and be pulled by the others.

Why do they join together?

Simple, because they share a common goal of trying to create some distance between themselves and the pack. Sounds like a business, doesn't it. Does it work? There are reports that the reduction in drag can be dramatic: "... in the middle of a well-developed group it can be as much as 40 %." The energy savings from drafting is huge, but it also has a significant impact on the group's overall productivity and speed. This is an excellent example of working smart rather than working hard.

Working hard would be every rider riding as fast and as hard as s/he can for the entire race. On the surface, this seems logical but anyone who knows about the physical demands of cycling knows that this would quickly lead to fatigue and the eventual breakdown of the riders.

Yet, this is exactly what happens every day in businesses around the world. Rather than strategically shifting work demands to allow each member of the team to oscillate, most corporate teams perceive this as a sign of weakness and instead burn out perfectly capable team members. They work hard rather than smart.

How can you use the concept of drafting to help your team stay fresh and improve their productivity?

What is the benefit to the team and the organization of strategically oscillating your team members?

In discussions with our clients, we ask them to share how they would implement the Tignum Recovery strategies within their team and their organization. Following are some solutions that they have identified to develop a team or organizational Performance Recovery approach:

_Schedule meetings to end at 15 minutes before the hour rather than always making them end on the hour. This will provide some time to recover from one meeting and change gears for the next meeting.

_Plan breaks in long meetings so continuous meeting time never exceeds 90 minutes at a time.

_Set up a Recovery room on each floor with some noise-proof headphones, a mat to take a power nap or stretch, a stability ball (for movement), and perhaps a hydration and strategic snack bar.

_Encourage team Recovery breaks. Many teams comment that smokers take frequent breaks to smoke, but nonsmokers are perceived as lazy when they stand outside for a break. Instead, call them Recovery breaks and encourage them (without the smoking, of course). When the team takes them together, they gain acceptance.

_Encourage power naps. You may need to develop a clever sign that lets others know not to interrupt a team member for the 15 minutes they are turning fully off.

_Develop Recovery buddies who remind each other to take consistent breaks.

_Encourage no e-mail messages on weekends and evenings, unless it's an emergency.

How can you incorporate some of these Recovery strategies in your team?

How about in your organization?

Recovery Instead of Smoking Rooms

In a recent discussion with a group of clients, we asked the question: How can you, as leaders in your organization, impact the sustainable performance of your company, or at least your direct section?

The group was sent out to discuss this topic in small teams and then came back to the larger group to present their thoughts and ideas. During our discussion the following questions came up:

Why do companies provide (at a significant expense) smoking rooms for workers but not Recovery rooms?

Why is it okay for a person to take as many smoking breaks as they want during the day, but if someone wants to take a power nap or go for a walk for a break the company culture sees that as a negative?
Why do some companies provide all the free candy or ice cream you want eat, but it's a stretch to get more than one apple a week?
Can you imagine what would happen if every boss sent out a memo stating: Weekends are for Recovery—no e-mail allowed?
Would these small changes to the workplace help team members become sustainable high performers?
These questions all led to more ideas and dialogue, and although the questions aren't always easy to answer, it does remind me of one thing. When we think differently and ask uncommon kinds of questions, we will eventually come up with some sustainable high performance answers.
Tignum Blog

Bringing Tignum to the Team

Some leaders immediately understand the need for sustainable high performance, and Alan Johnson, Chief Auditor of Unilever, is one of these leaders. As soon as Johnson was introduced to our work with sustainable high performance, he knew that Tignum was a strategic-must for his teams. After all, the audit job is one of the most demanding and challenging jobs within Unilever.

In an audit, a team is sent to a specific location to thoroughly audit the practices and policies of that business unit. As you can imagine, not every business unit leader is happy to get audited. To make it even more challenging, the people that perform the audits often have to stay on location for up to six weeks at a time. The travel demands are immense, the workloads are never-ending, and the attention to detail required for the task is mind-boggling.

When we first met Johnson and his team, the positive impact that the leader's Mindset had on his team was quite evident. There was a genuine commitment that Johnson made to his teams' performance and every person's vitality. In fact, Johnson stressed the importance of every member taking what they had learned from Tignum and implementing it at home as much as at work. He emphasized the need to be a high performer everywhere in your life since no one deserves your best more than your family.

At Tignum, we believe that sustainable high performance is about performing well in life—this means at work and away from work. Alan Johnson understood this philosophy and obviously lives it. He was so committed to the need for sustainable high performance that he pledged that every member of every audit team in Unilever would work with Tignum to develop the best individual and team strategies. As he put it, "These guys and girls give their lives to Unilever for over two years. They pick up and go anywhere that they are asked to. They work long hours and they produce great work. This job takes an enormous toll on everyone, and I know that the investment of sending everyone through the Tignum program will pay huge dividends."

Over the past three years, Tignum has trained every single member of the Unilever audit teams. In our work, we have challenged the teams to implement their Performance Mindset, Performance Nutrition, Performance Movement, and Performance Recovery strategies as a group to experience the difference it would make. The results of their team approach is described in the account below.

Simple Things Done Savagely Well

The Vietnam audit began with a high performance kick-off because the audit director Ram Mallya set an excellent example from the start. He assigned one member of his team to Mindset, one to Nutrition, one to Movement, and one to Recovery. Each one of these leaders was given the latitude to manage and support their strategies however they saw fit.

To address Mindset, the team completed a mind-mapping chart of the main Mindset elements that would be required to be sustainable high performers throughout this audit. They set up a jar that was used to collect payments from anyone who made a negative statement. Every Friday night, these proceeds were used for some celebration (the 80–20 Guideline in action). Next, they agreed to help each other mentally rehearse and prepare for each presentation and meeting that they had throughout the audit. Finally, each morning, they set some daily intentions and also took the time to recognize the things they did well the day before.

To address Nutrition, the team members reminded everyone of the need to stay hydrated. They purchased a refillable one-liter bottle for each person so they could measure how much water they were actually drinking. They planned high performance snacks and made them available throughout the audit. Next, they identified the best (high performance) places to eat and let everyone on the team know where these were. Then they reminded each other at the beginning of the audit about the proper portion sizes (using their hands as the guide). Finally, they planned for their 20% celebration time by having dessert, a beer, or something that was purely a pleasure food.

To address Movement, the team looked for every opportunity to walk. They walked to and from the audit, they took the stairs every chance they could, and they reminded each other to take breaks, and get up and move throughout the day. They encouraged everyone in the group to participate as a team in some tennis ball massage and the Daily Prep movements three days a week. They did a fantastic job of incorporating movement into their daily activities. They also planned dinner one hour later than usual so those that wanted could go for a run or complete the No Excuse Workout prior to eating.

To address Recovery, the team put up sticky notes that read, "Work smart. Rest hard." This was to remind everyone that rest was as important as work. They recommended everyone take two breathing breaks a day, one in the morning and one in the afternoon. They set up some mats in their room so that everyone could take a short power nap after lunch. This was a big hit and a powerful energizer that helped them get the most out of their afternoons.

At the end of this audit, following is the e-mail message that Tignum received:

Hi Scott,

I've just returned from holiday after my audit in Vietnam.

This was the first time I experienced an audit where the whole team fully embraced the Tignum strategies. At the onset, the team members agreed to volunteer as champions to lead each of the various Tignum pillars (Mindset, Nutrition, Movement, and Recovery). We held daily movement sessions, set aside an area for power naps, had nutritious snacks, etc., and all of these strategies were sustained throughout the audit. It worked and it made for a positive and effective team. In my view, it had an impact beyond our expectations by making us less stressed and much more efficient.

There is nothing new here, but it's clear that implementing these strategies has an impact on our abilities at an individual and team level. Having one motivated person in a team is great, but when everyone is firing on all cylinders, it sure does make a difference.

Regards,
RC

This is a real-world example of how one team implemented Performance Mindset, Performance Nutrition, Performance Movement, and Performance Recovery strategies to improve the productivity of their team. Your teams may implement strategies in different ways that work better for them based upon their make-up, their expertise, and the nature of their challenges. The point is that you understand the importance and benefits of taking a team approach to improving the team's, as well as each individual's, sustainability and performance.

How can your team consistently implement Mindset, Nutrition, Movement, and Recovery strategies to make it a high performing team?

Chapter Eighteen
Is Your Organization Sinking, Floating, or Swimming?

"It is not the strongest of the species that survives, nor the most intelligent that survives. It is the one that is the most adaptable to change."
Charles Darwin, English Naturalist

It is often an assumption that leaders can energize their teams with charisma alone, but this is a false premise. This is as foolish as thinking you can grow a bountiful garden with organic seeds and lousy soil. The truth is that a high performing organization can only be built by developing a high performance culture.

As noted previously, a common misperception is that having a full battery is all that you need to be a high performer. The problem is that there are a mountain of daily events that can easily run your battery down. Nothing can do this more than a low performance, or sinking, organizational culture.

Full battery
+ High performance habits
+ High performance cluture
= Sustainable high performance

Low battery
+ High performance demands
+ Low performance cluture
= Predictable low performance

Most organizations describe their culture in their mission statement, internal training manuals, or press releases. Unfortunately, reality does not always match the described organizational culture. The real culture is the one that every employee operates within, feels daily, and knows is present. The real organizational culture often flies under the radar, yet it definitely impacts all performance.

One of the world's renowned nutrition, health, and wellness companies has a beautiful glass building on the shore of Lake Geneva. The architecture is awe-inspiring and the view of this building is stunning. In fact, as you approach it, you can see through the lobby to a lush, colorful garden and the glimmering lake behind it.

During a meeting there, we made an interesting observation. After almost two hours, we realized that we had not seen one person outside in the garden. Not one person went outside for a walk, for a conversation, not even for a smoke. Alarmed by this observation, we asked our meeting host why there were no employees taking advantage of this inspiring natural environment.

"Are you crazy?" he replied. "We work in an all-glass building. If employees were to walk outside, everyone would wonder why they weren't getting their work done. Everyone would say that they must not have enough work to do."

As he heard his own words, he started to chuckle and added: "I guess, after presenting your Tignum approach, this attitude must seem pretty dysfunctional."

We laughed with him and shared that this is a problem in too many organizations. After all, taking a short walk outside is an effective way to clear your mind, stretch your legs, recover from work stress, and significantly improve your performance. Yet, organizations often do not support or encourage many of the simple high performance strategies we have presented.

What would you think if you saw someone at your office taking a Movement break?

What is the attitude of your organizational culture towards employees using Recovery breaks and oscillation strategies such as taking a power nap or doing some breathing exercises?

Are foods at your events strategically chosen to enhance performance or are they selected because they are inexpensive or easy to get?

What is the attitude of your organizational culture toward negative talk, rumors, internal stories full of unnecessary drama, or awfulizing?

Being aware of your own individual biases, as well as your organizational beliefs, is the first step to changing the culture. The next step is moving from knowing to doing.

What Stops Organizations From Taking Action?

Working with organizations worldwide, we have been bombarded by the resounding positive response for the need of sustainable high performance strategies in business. Leaders share story after story of key players within their organizations who are sinking. Even worse, they also see the negative shift where more and more executives are struggling just to stay afloat. Despite these experiences and concerns, we still encounter resistance to take action when we get in front of a group of decision makers. It's not logical resistance but rather habitual resistance —a reflex that comes with naturally defending the status quo and habitually rejecting any new idea, program, or change.

What stops you from thinking differently when it comes to sustainable high performance?

Where does your resistance come from?

We have noticed some trends to this resistance and have categorized them into five basic categories:

_Shareholder Value Hurdle
_It's-a-Tough-Time Hurdle
_Incentive Hurdle
_Return on Investment Hurdle
_Perception Hurdle

The Shareholder Value Hurdle

This is probably the toughest hurdle to get over because the driving forces behind it are not always rational. As stock prices are influenced by the emotions of the market, leaders are continually being pressured to increase the shareholder value. The common mantra is: Increase revenues, decrease costs, create a compelling success story, and do it yesterday. Even when organizations meet their projected revenues, there is no guarantee that shareholders will respond positively. This irrational, and at times unpredictable, relationship can make a CEO and the executive board crazy. This confusion can lead to decisions that increase the immediate stress, to obtain short-term gains at the sacrifice of long-term sustainable high performance.

We believe that the Tignum strategies we have shared not only give shareholders the best chance for short-term success but also the only chance for sustainable success. In order to achieve this success, organizations need more productive teams and a more productive workforce. Increasing shareholder value should also mean improved productivity in all areas of the business system from research and development to production, marketing, and sales. Improving productivity requires energy, passion, creativity, perceptive thinking, focus, innovation, resilience, and capacity. Yet, very few organizations strategically invest in and develop these qualities within their leadership ranks, their corporate culture, or their workforce.

Throughout our coaching with clients, one theme that is consistently shared with us is that corporate life in most large companies is psychologically toxic. Too often, executives find themselves in no-win situations trying to do more with less, while running on empty.

This is why in challenging times the knee-jerk reaction to immediately cut employee development programs makes absolutely no sense. As C. K. Prahalad noted in our earlier interview, "This reflects very short-term thinking and it is business suicide." Bernhard Lobmueller, a retired IBM executive, also agrees: "Sustainable high performance programs should be the second to last thing that is cut. The last thing should be the toilet paper."

The good news is that venture capitalists and market analysts are beginning to inquire about the sustainable high performance of the leaders within a company. Some companies are even developing long-term bonus structures for CEOs that require the assessment of the long-term consequences of their policies and programs. This will hopefully lead CEOs and executive boards to realize that the investment in the energy, resilience, brain performance, and capacity of their leadership (and their workforce) is the only way to increase shareholder value, in the short- and long-term.

The It's-a-Tough-Time Hurdle

This hurdle is especially visible in challenging times but it is an excuse used in any climate. Organizations are always in a tough time. It's a tough time because raw material prices are up. It's a tough time because fuel prices are up. It's a tough time because we are in the middle of a reorganization or retooling. It's a tough time because we just got a new CEO, and s/he is going to change everything.

Invariably, when we engage leaders within an organization in the discussion of the need for sustainable high performance, they throw up the it's-a-tough-time card. Now is not the right time to discuss this option, they say, because we are in a very tough time. The problem is that NOW is exactly the time to discuss sustainable high performance, because if you don't address it now, there will be an even bigger crisis in the future.

Consider the following example when evaluating your tough time:

If there is a building on fire and you see a firetruck responding, you may sigh with relief because you know that help is on the way. But what if the firefighting team on the truck is understaffed, inadequately trained, physically exhausted, mentally unprepared, or simply burned out?

Just because you see the firetruck going to the burning building doesn't mean the people in the building will be rescued or that the fire will be put out in the most efficient and productive way. Yes, eventually all fires do go out! But some burn down four blocks of buildings, spew off toxic chemicals, and kill lots of people in the process.

This is true in business, too, that eventually all fires will go out. But, we ask you to consider: What is the cost? The only way to truly solve a tough time, to move from sinking to swimming (high performance and profitability), is to be sure that the people who need to fight the fires are high performers. This means you need to invest in a solid foundation to build their energy, resilience, brain performance, and capacity.

In our research, we have estimated that approximately 95 % of all executives are currently either floating (80 %) or sinking (15 %). This means they are not performing at their full potential and more than likely are costing your organization money. We estimate this cost to be between 27,000 to 45,000 euros ($38,000 to $63,000 US) per person per year. And all of this data was collected in normal economic times. This is startling when you consider the investment that an organization makes in these leaders in terms of salary, benefits, and development. These figures make it a tough time for any organization, regardless of the economic times.

The Incentive Hurdle

High performers deserve compensation for their hard work and their contributions to the organization. In fact, many organizations use incentives to inspire leaders to meet their financial or performance goals. Sometimes these incentives include lavish trips, high-end conferences, or even luxurious team retreats. In good times, most of these incentive packages went unnoticed and were socially acceptable. But times have changed and today public (and shareholder) scrutiny is intense. The problem is, who gets to determine what is lavish, what is excessive, what is an incentive, and what is absolutely necessary to improve performance?

In the absence of clear criteria, many organizations take the all-or-none approach. Unfortunately, this is shortsighted and can have a huge performance cost to the organization, to the shareholders, and in certain cases, to the entire economy. When the stakes are high and high performance is a must, organizations must invest in the high performance of its leaders. This investment in these leaders is not an incentive—it is a strategic necessity.

As we've shared throughout this book, many leaders realize that their leadership teams are definitely sliding towards sinking due to the inordinate pressures they face and their lack of sustainable high performance strategies. But the dilemma, they say, is that if they were to attend a two-day sustainable high performance program, the perception may be that they were frolicking at a resort at the cost of the business' success.

Leaders get paid to make tough decisions and to stand up to defend these decisions. This is true even in tough times and even when public scrutiny is high. In our opinion, there is no decision more important than investing in the sustainable high performance of the organization's most vital asset—its talent. This is not a lavish incentive; it's a strategic-must.

The Return on Investment Hurdle

There is a big challenge when it comes to measuring return on investment (ROI). In the infamous words of Albert Einstein: "Not everything that counts can be counted; and not everything that can be counted, counts." Think of leadership development programs, or high potential programs, or even project management training programs. Do these programs work? How do you know? The only way you can truly be sure would be to perform controlled studies with groups that participated in the training and those that didn't. But how often can a company afford to do this? The problem is that most companies are extremely dynamic, and therefore they can't land the plane to fix it; they have to fix it while it continues to fly.

In Beyond HR: The New Science of Human Capital, John W. Boudreau and Peter M. Ramstad examined the challenges associated with standard ROI measurements. In one of their findings, they state: "Typical ROI calculations focus on one HR investment at a time and fail to consider how those investments work together as a portfolio. Training may produce value beyond its cost, but would that value be even higher if it were combined with proper investments in individual incentives related to the training outcomes? Understanding ROI and putting it into a decision context requires a framework that distinguishes and integrates efficiency, effectiveness, and impact."

Is it possible to measure the ROI of improving the energy, resilience, brain performance, and capacity of leaders and their teams?

We believe that there is a way, but we also recognize the plethora of confounding factors. First, these factors are the foundation of all performance. Therefore, it is difficult to measure these in isolation of all other types of performance enhancement programs such as leadership development, negotiation skill training, and project management training. Second, business performance is impacted by many external factors such as the economy, world events, the fluctuations of the stock market, and the cost of materials and fuel. How can these be factored into ROI calculations?

In 2006, we worked with a global HR leadership team. It was a very trying time as the company was in the middle of a large reorganization that involved significant workforce reductions, as well as a complex outsourcing of some key HR functions. The stress was enormous, and several team members were on the verge of burnout. The team leader brought Tignum in because he was afraid that it would get worse.

Almost three years later, we asked this leader if our work had helped his team. At first, he paused and replied honestly that he wasn't really sure. After a moment of contemplation, he answered: "In the last three years, the demands on my team have drastically increased. The speed in which they must act has increased and so has their responsibility. But in these most challenging times, my team is doing great. They have more energy, they're passionate about their jobs, they're engaged, and they're healthy. Definitely the strategies we learned from Tignum played a big part in that."

We believe that ROI should be measured in ways that provide more accurate results. But, perhaps the more important questions are:

How well do you (and your team members) perform when your energy is low, you are exhausted, you have brain fog, and you can't focus?

What is the cost to your team or organization if leaders are lower performers?

What is the benefit if your leaders are sustainable high performers?

What happens if your pivotal players suffer burnout? What happens to the stock prices? What happens to the morale and productivity of your entire team?

The Perception Hurdle

Almost every leader will have to lead significant cost-cutting initiatives. This usually means taking the pressure they receive from the board, or CEO, and implementing cost-cutting strategies throughout their teams. These cuts often present major challenges for everybody involved.

At the same time, good leaders know that they should do something to develop, support, and energize their teams. Unfortunately, stopping the speed train for even two days for these teams, to invest in their sustainable high performance, could be perceived as the opposite of cost cutting. Even if it leads to a real improvement in the team's performance and decreases the costs of presenteeism and mediocre productivity, many leaders are afraid. They are afraid of the perception of being weak, of spending money when they have been told to cut spending, and of "taking a break" when the demands are high. As many leaders have privately shared with us, they know they need to invest in their leaders and their teams to make them swimmers, but if they do they will get fired. And we ask: Is this just perception or is reality?

What are you willing to do to improve the performance and sustainability of your teams?

The second element to the perception hurdle is what we presented at the beginning of this book. When you see the words Mindset, Nutrition, Movement, and Recovery, what is your response? Do you perceive these as critical for impacting your personal and team's performance? Or do you perceive them to influence only your health and your wellness?

The problem with perception is that it becomes the lens through which you see things. Your perception will become your reality. If there is one message we hope you get from this book, it is that the total integration of your Mindset, Nutrition, Movement, and Recovery habits will determine whether you sink, float, or swim. The reality is that this is not a health or wellness issue—it is a performance issue and it will determine your future.

You may want to consider: What is the perception of your clients, your share-holders, and your strategic partners when your leaders are floaters? What would the benefit be to your brands and your talent acquisition if your organization was perceived as a swimmer? Successful and sustainable leaders understand that they should advertise the investments they make in the sustainable high performance of their organization, not hide them.

Maximize Human Performance by Optimizing Culture

Over the past 20 years, there has been a huge evolution in business technology in order to optimize organizations' efficiency and increase productivity. Today, we need to work towards optimizing human performance and the organizational culture. Becoming a swimmer yourself is important, but creating a swimming organizational culture is the only way to truly win in this competitive market.

So what are the critical elements for implementing sustainable high performance on an organizational level?

The first element has to be the full buy-in and participation of the CEO and her/his senior leadership team. When these influential leaders begin to demonstrate a high level of sustainable energy, an authentic resilience, an expanded capacity, and a High Performance Mindset on a daily basis, both the shareholders and organizational leadership will take notice. This is a huge step in overcoming inertia.

The next step is to infuse sustainable high performance strategies into the senior leaders direct report leadership teams (leaders from across the functional areas of an organization). These teams are usually where the rubber meets the road when it comes to driving corporate change. It's at this level that organizational transformation happens when these leaders are passionate, engaged, alert, creative, and solution-oriented. But this can only happen if they have the necessary Performance Mindset, Performance Nutrition, Performance Movement, and Performance Recovery habits.

Finally, you need to develop an organization-wide strategy to integrate sustainable high performance as the red thread through all organizational functions. This strategy must take into account that one size will not fit all. The approach needs to be multifaceted, pragmatic, and doable at all levels of the organization. Following are some strategies that have worked with our clients:

Respect individuality. If there is one thing we have learned, it is that everyone is different. We all bring our own experiences, our own baggage, our own needs and our own desires. One guaranteed way to fail is the I'm-a-marathoner-so-everyone-should-run-a-marathon-together approach. Therefore, if a performance enhancement program is going to be successful it needs to be individualized.

Understand behavioral change. As we noted earlier, change doesn't happen because of SMART goals; it comes out of emotion, emotion, and more emotion. Therefore, the implementation of an organization-wide sustainable high performance program must be authentic and speak to people's emotions and feelings. People won't change because they know they should; they'll change because they feel they want to.

Focus on benefits rather than change. Every change process will create some pain, but if it's right then the benefits will outweigh the pain. Therefore, the campaign, the messaging, and most of the discussions have to focus on the benefits of achieving your full potential.

Make it easy to practice the habits. Human beings naturally take the path of least resistance. Therefore, if you want your organization's performance to improve, you have to make it easy for your members to practice the habits you have learned throughout this book. If the organization Recovery room is in the farthest corner of the campus, chances are that no one will use it, and they will doubt the commitment of the leadership.

Design your office space for high performance. Create the proper physical and emotional space for high performance to grow and develop. Some factors to consider are lighting, air flow, furniture, colors, layout, and access to open spaces.

Proactively design your culture. We have covered some factors that influence an organizational culture, but you really need a director of sustainable high performance. Too often organizations create policies, procedures, and programs that send conflicting messages to the workforce, and this ultimately destroys trust and commitment. Therefore, you should create an organized and orchestrated approach to making your organizational culture a high performance culture. You also need to be proactive and do it before your organization starts sinking.

Integrate all four pillars. At Tignum, we have had our clients share story after story of attempts they have made to improve their energy and resilience by only focusing on one pillar such as nutrition or exercise. Unfortunately, their attempts always end in failure. Human beings are complex and we live as an integrated unit; therefore, we have to approach our sustainable high performance in an integrated fashion. To be successful, you need to integrate simple strategies from all of the Performance Mindset, Nutrition, Movement, and Recovery pillars.

Focus on performance, not on health. Many organizations have implemented great health programs but as we discussed earlier, these programs are designed to prevent you from sinking rather than helping you swim. A performance program moves sinkers and floaters towards becoming swimmers. Additionally, many of our clients are apprehensive to share their medical information with their boss, or even their company doctor. Performance, on the other hand, is an organizational issue, and it is easy to focus on performance in a noninvasive and supportive way. Note that a good performance program does not devalue the importance of good health; it merely takes a more proactive and less sensitive approach.

Keep it fun. When we talk about high performance, it is easy to think that it's all work. In Section V, we discussed the importance of laughter for Recovery and the importance of fun for intrinsic motivation. The fact is that very few changes will last if it is not fun to be part of the change.

Practice what you preach. This may sound a little cliché but it rings true over and over again. There is nothing that will destroy the implementation of an organizational sustainable high performance program faster than seeing the leadership say one thing and do another. For this reason, it's paramount that the leaders model the high performance habits they want their teams to develop.

Make sustainable high performance part of the employee value proposition (EVP). Exceptional organizations value their talent, and one way to demonstrate that is to commit to their employees' energy, resilience, brain performance, and capacity. Financial packages can definitely attract talent but they rarely keep talent. Talented leaders know that they are always in demand. They also know that they can frequently negotiate better deals elsewhere. What high performers value is being in an organization that supports them to achieve their full potential. This means not simply talking about how important employees are—it means proving it.

Include expectations and benchmarks for sustainable high performance on annual performance reviews and in the bonus structure. Reward swimmers (not just for their performance but for their habits) more than floaters. (This makes sense since they probably contribute more to your profitability). This also means that you should reward leaders that contribute to making the organizational culture more high performance.

Gut Check

By reviewing the following descriptors of sinking, floating, or swimming cultures, you can identify the things you can easily change within your organization to move your culture more towards swimming. Incredible organizational potential lies within reach if you are willing to shift from just knowing to doing.

Does your organization want to sink, float, or swim?

The choice is always yours.

Your organizational culture is **sinking** when …

_there is a team Mindset that is negative and problem-focused
_leaders foster negativity by ignoring it or buying into it
_leaders hold back one-on-one feedback and instead criticize through rumors
_many people use coffee as the drug of choice to make it through the day
_the organization provides only high-sugar or processed food for snacks
_there are long, unproductive meetings without breaks where people are
   distracted and not engaged
_leaders perceive Recovery breaks as a sign of laziness or weakness
_the working environment cultivates individualism rather than collaboration
_leaders criticize rather than support personal innovation
_no one is held accountable
_the focus is placed on being busy rather than getting results
_personal development and sustainable high performance programs are the
   first to be cut during tough budget times
_there is a mission that states that human resources are the priority, but all of
   the organizational actions contradict this statement
_leaders and team members are unaware that Mindset, Nutrition, Movement,
   and Recovery habits impact the energy, resilience, brain performance, and
   capacity of the team or organization

Your organizational culture is **floating** when ...

_there is a fluctuating team Mindset that changes from moment to moment
_leaders talk about trust and empathy but their actions don't always match
_leaders talk about the importance of authentic feedback but then criticize it
_snacks for meetings are chosen for convenience or cost rather than for their
impact on performance
_leaders talk about not working through lunch but then plan or expect
working lunches
_there is discussion about making meetings more productive and strategic
but no follow-through
_recovery rooms are provided but there is no support for people to use them
_leaders avoid dealing with conflict whenever they can
_leaders talk about the need to work smart rather than hard, but then criticize
people for taking breaks
_personal development programs are seen as nice-to-have, not a
strategic-must
_there is a mission that states that human resources are the priority, but many
of the organizational actions contradict this statement
_leaders only address sustainable high performance of team members when
there is a crisis within the team (such as a burnout)
_leaders and team members are somewhat aware that Mindset, Nutrition,
Movement, and Recovery habits are important but do not make the connection with performance

Your organizational culture is **swimming** when ...

_there is a team Mindset that is positive and solution-focused
_leaders challenge negativity by reframing it in the positive
_leaders provide authentic and productive feedback
_all members are encouraged to mentally and physically prepare for
must-win events
_the organization supports Performance Nutrition and provides high
performance foods
_there are highly productive meetings with high performance hydration
options and snacks, and scheduled strategic breaks
_there are many opportunities created for members to move throughout
the day
_leaders expect and support members to take regeneration breaks
and power naps
_there is support across the organization for personal innovation
_leaders approach setbacks and change as opportunities
_everyone is held accountable and there is a results-only work environment
_the actions of the organization prove every day that its people are the
most important asset
_there is a high performance work environment that implements
performance reviews and employee value propositions
_leaders and team members integrate Mindset, Nutrition, Movement,
and Recovery strategies to effectively utilize the energy, resilience, brain
performance, and capacity of the team or organization

At Tignum, we operate on the premise that simple things done savagely well can produce significant and long-lasting results. This is how a high performance culture is built, one simple thing at a time. But it is essential to remember that cultures are made up of individuals, and therefore, everyone has the ability and responsibility to make the organization better.

How will you take responsibility to make your organization productive and profitable?

What role will you play in building a sustainable high performance culture?

Chapter Nineteen
Time to Dive In

"Sustainable high performance doesn't happen by chance—it happens by choice."

The world is rapidly evolving and the demands are growing exponentially. The strategies that you used to get yourself to this point probably will not be enough to help you succeed in the future. There will be new pressures and challenges, and they will either help you reach your potential (swim), keep you comfortably numb (float), or they will crush you (sink). You get to choose.

In an interview with Rita McGrath, PhD, Columbia Business School Associate Professor and consultant for Global 500 companies, she discussed the importance of managing your focus and integrating information: "The information age has changed the way you get information, process information, and deal with interruptions. You used to have just a few TV channels and one phone line. Now you have infinite sources of information and it's not about managing distractions, it's about managing your focus. You have to be able to get all the information you need and then quickly integrate it into your strategy."

Unfortunately, this can be particularly overwhelming and exhausting if you don't have high performance habits. Similarly, as we noted in the previous chapter, corporate environments can be psychologically toxic. Not because of an inherent deceit or dysfunction, but rather from the sheer complexity and bureaucracy that comes when many people with diverse backgrounds, cultures, personalities, and expertise try to work towards a common solution. In these environments, personal control must be redefined, and measurements of personal achievement and success must be redrawn.

Focus on What You Want to Grow
I remember an interview with Andre Agassi on a terribly windy day when a reporter asked
him if the wind bothered him. Agassi smiled and replied: Wind? I didn't even notice the wind.
I grew up in Las Vegas where it's always windy. I love the wind. His response seems ironic,
when you consider that Agassi's opponent blamed his own loss on the terrible weather
conditions.
What's the wind that is drawing your focus and ruining your performance?
After working with thousands of executives, I'm convinced that many people don't take
responsibility for their own focus. Or perhaps they're not always aware of where they have
placed their focus. If you really want to quickly improve your performance, take control of
your focus and place it only on what you want to grow.
Tignum Blog

Reframe Your Perspective

Like Andre Agassi's experience, whatever you focus on will grow. Unfortunately, right now too many executives are focusing on the negative economy, the stock exchange fluctuations, the layoffs, the cutbacks, and the internal struggles. If you focus on these, you will find plenty of reasons to be afraid, to be exhausted, and to simply want to give up. But if you take the Agassi approach and you focus on the things that you can control (especially your own personal high performance strategies), you will realize that there are many opportunities for excellence.

One of our clients summed it up best, when he shared, "I sit on my commute home every night and I ask myself: 'Am I being the best boss I can be? Am I being the best husband I can be? Am I being the best father I can be?' And when I think of the answers, I get frustrated and demoralized."

The truth is that the answer to these questions is often no. Not because leaders are not trying, but rather because they don't have the energy to give their best efforts, or perhaps their image of perfection is unrealistic.

On the contrary, if you reframe these questions, suddenly there is not only a light at the end of the tunnel, there's an opportunity for you to realize that this is a work in progress, and every day you get a new chance to make better choices for you, your team, and your organization.

In reframing your perspective, consider the following:

Did you implement the habits to create and maximize your energy?

Did you focus on the things you could control today?

Did you do something for yourself today in order to expand your capacity, move towards your potential, and increase your impact?

Did you do everything that you know how to do to prepare yourself to successfully compete in your must-win events today?

Did you do something to positively impact your team or your organization?

Did you bring energy to those you influence?

Why is your organization better today because you came to work?

There is no doubt that all indicators point to the business world of tomorrow being full of challenges; and it will be exhausting for those who aren't prepared. But when our clients focus on the questions above, they quickly realize that by incorporating simple habits in Performance Mindset, Performance Nutrition, Performance Movement, and Performance Recovery, they can be more prepared to meet their daily challenges and move their teams and organizations towards sustainable high performance.

One person who is reframing his perspective, especially when it comes to selecting the companies in which he will invest is Kurt Ehmann, Financial Advisor for Financial Network in Los Angeles. Ehmann states: "I tell my clients that they should be investing their money in the companies that are continuing to invest in the high performance of their leaders and their workforce. These are the companies that will have the power and the energy to be innovative and to execute their business model. These are the companies that are going to catapult out of this recession and who are going to give you the greatest returns on your investments. Right now, I'm doing my research to find the companies that are not buried in short-term crisis thinking but who are boldly looking to the future. With everyone's share prices down, these companies are going to be the prime investment opportunities."

Prepare for the Future

Yes, the world is changing and you must be prepared to change with it. A recent report predicted employment trends for the next 12 years. The projected trend is that very few workers will be able to retire at current retirement ages of 59 to 64.

Why? Due to the challenges businesses are facing with the Generation Y workforce, older executives will be asked to continue working to provide leadership and experience. With the market sensitivity and the growing debt of many nations, it is unlikely that the current government retirement benefit plans will remain solvent enough to support our current retirement ages. Finally, with the progress of modern medicine, the life expectancy is growing longer and longer.

Can you imagine ...

Working as hard as you do today when you are in your 70s?

But aside from just living longer, there are other trends that will surely change the way we work. The current recession has led to record layoffs as organizations have been forced to downsize. These new, leaner organizations will be forced to do more with less people. This means the days of working harder and harder until you eventually burnout and retire are gone. The new paradigm will be dependent upon leaders, executives, and workers who have sustainable high performance habits and who work in high performance cultures. Everyone will have to be a swimmer, since organizations that are made up of floaters will certainly not survive.

Are your habits currently capable of giving you the energy and resilience you will need for the future?

Is your organizational culture going to energize your executives or zap their energy?

Are you a swimmer or are you a floater?

Finally, as organizations get smaller there will be a growing number of consultants, freelancers, and independent problem-solvers who will be called in on a project-by-project basis to create winning solutions. You may become one of these free-lancers yourself.

In this situation, companies won't provide benefits or long-term security, so each consultant will be responsible for her/his own sustainable high performance. In this new business world, the opportunities for those who can produce and those who can consistently swim will be incredible. They will get paid well and they will have the freedom to take on only the assignments that interest them.

Today, and in the future, the scarce resource will be human energy, human brain power, and human ability. The environmental challenges, the economic challenges, and the social challenges we will face will require an abundance of high performing leaders. You will need the Performance Mindset, Performance Nutrition, Performance Movement, and Performance Recovery habits to have the energy, resilience, and focus you will need. Without these, you will have no passion, and that will be the worst crisis of all.

"Successful and unsuccessful people do not vary greatly in their abilities. They vary in their desires to reach their potential."
John Maxwell, International Leadership Expert and Author

Why Waste Your Potential?

We chose the following letter as an ending because it is honest and telling ... a description of one client's journey, complete with his challenges, triumphs, and passion for wanting to perform better.

Dear Scott, Jogi, and the entire Tignum Team,

I am writing this letter to share my thoughts and gratitude after working with Tignum. Before I worked with Tignum, I was overwhelmed with work, home pressures, and my own doubts. Our global team was new, and there was friction among the group. The negative team dynamics were draining almost all of us. My wife and I were also struggling, and for the first time in my life, I was beginning to doubt my capabilities.

After the first evening of your program I felt great. What we had learned about our behavioral styles, our testing results, and all of the Tignum pillars was quite eye-opening. What shocked me the most, though, were the discussions that we all had at dinner. We were talking about our team mindset, achieving our potential, appreciating each other's differences, and sharing our own personal strengths and what we brought to the team. Even more surprising, members of our team who had not been proponents of exercise or healthy eating were talking about supporting each other and teaming up to help each other change their habits.

At the end of the next day, after a challenging 14 hours, we were all astonished at how much energy we still had. The movement sessions, the high performance meals and snacks, the power nap, the breathing breaks ... everything came together to make an unbelievably productive and life-changing day.

*The next day, we learned how to bring our new strategies together, and I have to admit that everything we learned and every tool we were given was immediately applicable. But what impacted me the most was the development of my personal innovation map. In the reflection time, I developed my **To Be** goals and for me, this was the turning point. It was during this exercise that I realized that I had the potential to be a great husband and father, a compassionate team leader, and an inspirational role model for my team.*

The shocker for me was when I realized that this Tignum work had really nothing to do with my marathon running (although I set a personal best marathon time four months later). It really had to do with my performance at work and at home. It was more about creating the best me and then sustaining it. I know it sounds corny, but there is nothing more liberating than looking in the mirror and realizing that you can and must be responsible for your own actions and solve your own challenges.

I must admit, though, that when I hit my first dip I lost all of my motivation and I almost panicked. Even though the Tignum coaches had warned us, I thought briefly that I was going to fail at a personal change plan yet again. But, you quickly got me back on track, and that dip became an excellent motivator for the next four months.

The total integration of Mindset, Nutrition, Movement, and Recovery strategies, along with some positive coaching and support, has changed my life. I saved my marriage, I transformed my team, I became a high performer, and it has been a blast.

It's been over two years now, and I have to admit that I am not perfect with utilizing my strategies. I have some good days, some great days, and even some pretty bad days. But now, I am aware of my habits and their consequences so I don't panic. I just get back on track the next day.

The thing is, I have more energy at work and I get more done in less time because I'm so focused. I feel much better, even though I'm getting older. You challenged us in the beginning to see if we could be better in five years than we were on that first day, and I have to humbly admit, I'm on my way.

Thanks to all of you at Team Tignum. What you have done for me and my team has been amazing!

Tignum Client

All Habits Begin With One Step

So how do you move yourself, your team, and your organization forward? Throughout this book, we have posed many reflective questions to help improve your awareness and begin developing a plan. We have also given you practical tips and examples of high performance strategies. In addition, at the end of each section, we have provided you with a way to measure whether you, your team, or your organizational culture are sinking, floating, or swimming. These tools, along with all the other information we have provided, will enable you, your team, and your organization to develop clear actions that you can build into daily life to improve the energy, resilience, brain performance, and capacity of your organization.

Finally, we have created a place on our website where you can get additional information. At Tignum, we are always researching which tools or strategies work best for our clients. By frequently visiting our website, you will be able to learn about these new strategies and tools, read our blogs, download our podcasts, and take your own sustainable high performance to a higher level.

It is important to remember is that there is no perfection. We don't live in a perfect world, and there is no such thing as a perfect person. Therefore, we recommend that you envision your sustainable high performance as a process or a work in progress. There is no end destination, because the benefits are cumulative and the process is dynamic.

When it comes to taking your first step to change your habits, we would like to leave you with the following words for action:

First, only you can change your habits. We can give you all the information, all the tools, and all the strategies, but ultimately only you can make it happen.

Second, change is a process AND the benefits are expansive. These benefits won't only impact you; they will also impact your family, your friends, your team, your company, and even your brand.

Third, setbacks are not only normal, they are predictable. They are also an effective source of motivation because they force you to recommit to your **To Be** goals and to the reasons why you want to change. In this process, you will find the most powerful intrinsic motivation ever.

Fourth, human beings are complex, and everything you do has a consequence on something else in your body or mind. Therefore, only an integrated solution will lead to lasting change. This approach doesn't require that you do everything, but it does require that you complete some small action in each one of the pillars.

Finally, we began this book with a dedication to all of our clients because YOU are what motivates us. Your sustainable high performance is truly our passion. When you share your stories, like the ones we have featured in this book, you don't simply make us happy; you help make us better at creating sustainable high performance strategies that work.

Every day, we discuss ways in which Tignum can more effectively serve our clients. Writing this book has played a large part in refining our vision and strategies, ultimately making us better at what we do. We thank each and every one of you for sharing in this experience. And we look forward to hearing from you in the future. Remember to check out our website at www.tignum.com for updated information, tools, blogs, podcasts, and more.

The choice is always yours.

Epilogue
The Tignum Story

Tignum – a Latin word meaning "beam"
illuminating you with new information, strategies, and motivations
(a beam of light); and supporting you especially during times of change
and challenge (a structural beam)

Epilogue
The Tignum Story

You may be wondering—what is Tignum, exactly? And, how did Jogi Rippel and Scott Peltin come together? What compelled us to act upon fulfilling this need for sustainable high performance strategies for executives and business leaders? How did a business entrepreneur and a firefighter from very different backgrounds, from countries that are across the Atlantic Ocean (Germany and the United States) meet and put together such a powerful concept?

Our clients frequently ask these questions, so we decided to end with a few vignettes that describe our journey to create Tignum.

Jogi

It was the spring of 1999 when my father entered his last year of work before retirement. It was also almost exactly a year before he planned to hand over his company, when he was diagnosed with cancer. My dad was an entrepreneur, and he worked hard his entire life with a clear focus to slow down when he finally retired. Only 18 months later, my dad passed away, and I'll never forget what he told me in one of the many conversations we had during his battle with cancer.

He said, "Jogi, please don't make the mistake I made. Don't disregard your own health and vitality like I did. It is your core asset. Don't take it for granted and don't wait until a crisis hits before you address it."

His words will stay with me for the rest of my life. And, my father's words were the beginning of a journey that would lead to the creation of Tignum.

Scott

From the first day that I walked into a fire station, I was motivated by the opportunity to impact other people's lives with my own high performance. I remember doing mental imagery exercises as I ran around Greenbelt Lake—picturing myself kicking in a door; making it down a dark, hot, and smoky hallway; and performing a rescue under the worst of conditions.

Throughout my years in the Fire Service, the idea of how to improve performance was more than just a curiosity to me; it was a burning passion. Even when some of the old-school guys challenged the benefits of mental training, the importance of functional training, the value of quality recovery on the fire ground, and the need to teach new firefighters how to deal with their stress and emotions; I was always driven to researching best practices and challenging the status quo.

Being blessed with a fantastic Fire Chief Alan Brunacini, in the Phoenix Fire Department I was fortunate to be able to explore and develop many different ideas on improving the mental, physical, and emotional development of firefighters. I was also fortunate to be a member of several national committees working to address key issues that were influencing the health, wellness, safety, and performance of firefighters across the United States.

Jogi

After my father died I knew that I had to rethink my career path. I had been an entrepreneur with my own marketing company before I attended the MBA program at IMD Business School in Lausanne, Switzerland. I wanted to have more impact. I saw my father's story being played over and over again with many of the corporate executives that were coming through IMD. They were working long hours, traveling constantly, and struggling with one corporate change initiative after another; and you could see the negative impact on their health and performance.

I would go for walks on the path around Lake Geneva and I would ask myself: Why do so many people wait until it's too late to make changes in their lifestyle habits? Why don't they see that they are sacrificing their performance at work and at home, as well as killing themselves simply to get ahead? I knew that it was too late to help my father, but I believed that finding the answers to these questions and helping these leaders learn a better way had to be the foundation of Tignum.

Throughout the early development of Tignum, I was fortunate to have the support of Professor Sean Meehan from IMD. He asked me to share my ideas with the new MBA students so that they could learn from my experiences and hopefully make some changes in their habits. It was during one of these presentations that I met Pieter-Christian van Oranje, a member of the Dutch Royal Family. He was an accomplished marathoner and a dedicated philanthropist, so the idea of helping business leaders improve their performance to deepen their impact really resonated with him.

Shortly after meeting Pieter-Christian, he and I decided to collaborate and develop the business plan for Tignum. We strategized who our potential clients would be and the partners we would need to make our deliverables world-class. We decided that I would travel to the US to meet with some possible high performance partners, and Pieter-Christian would work on opening some doors to potential clients. This led me to Athletes' Performance, the world leader in training elite athletes across a multitude of sports, in Tempe, Arizona.

Scott

When I was thinking about retiring from the Fire Service, I started exploring all the potential avenues I could think of. I had worked on the front line as a firefighter and as a captain. I had led several battalions and varied areas of the fire department, as a battalion and division chief. I spent 25 years developing programs to help firefighters and leaders in the Fire Service become high performers in the worst of situations under the highest levels of stress. Now it was time to see if what I had to share had any value outside the fire department.

A scientist by training, I did my research. I asked every executive I could find about the challenges he or she faced. What was a day in their shoes like? The answer was always the same. "I basically put out fires all day," they would reply.

"What training have you received on putting out fires?" I would respond. Their faces would go blank, their eyebrows would raise slightly, and almost every time they would smile just a bit and state "none." Interesting, I thought, because that was exactly what I had been trained to do for my entire adult life.

A short time later, I developed a presentation called "Igniting Personal Excellence" for the annual Phoenix Fire Department Health and Wellness Symposium. It was all about the elements that are necessary to ignite a fire. In the fire tetrahedron you need fuel, oxygen, heat, and a chain reaction in order for any fire to start. I immediately recognized that these same elements were necessary to achieve personal excellence. Fuel came from nutrition. Oxygen came from doing regular exercise. Heat came from having a purpose, passion, or mission in life. A chain reaction was either created or destroyed by the habits a person had, including sleep and stress management habits. And, as I began delivering this presentation around the country, I could see that this message resonated with my audiences, opening people's eyes to the things they needed to do to achieve their full potential.

At the same time, I was asked by Athletes' Performance to consult on the development of a firefighter physical training program. With the similarities of the demands of performing on the fire ground and on the athletic ground, it seemed a natural fit for Athletes' Performance to implement their methodology with firefighters. With my strong background in functional training, I was honored and intrigued to meet Mark Verstegen, the founder and president of Athletes' Performance. It was this set of circumstances that serendipitously led me to meet Jogi.

Jogi

When I got to Athletes' Performance I was very impressed with Mark Verstegen's passion for helping his athletes achieve their potential and extend their careers. Taking athletes who were already high performers and helping them take their performance to the next level while simultaneously improving their sustainability really inspired me. Both Mark and I immediately saw the parallel need in the business world. In addition, the COO of Athletes' Performance Dan Burns, a Harvard MBA graduate, joined us in our discussions as I explained my vision. Little did I know that this early vision paled in comparison to what Tignum would eventually become.

During my week in Arizona, I was able to experience what it felt like to be an athlete going through the Athletes' Performance methodology. As a former competitive tennis player I loved the systems they used, the approach of the highly professional coaches, and the strategic blend of work and rest that Mark had developed.

And, it was during a recovery break in the cold plunge that I met Scott. I remember looking across the frigid pool and asking him, "Why would a firefighter come train at Athletes' Performance?" Maybe it was hypothermia, or maybe it was Scott's witty response to my common-sense question, but I knew this guy had a different way of looking at things. He grinned (as only Scott can) and simply replied: "Would you rather have the firefighter who comes to save your life be a high performer or the overpaid athlete that you read about in the newspaper?"

Cold Plunge
A cold plunge is a small pool that is kept at approximately 55 °F (12.8 °C) and is used to help athletes improve the quality and speed of their recovery. The water is painfully cold and in the beginning, it is a struggle to stay immersed for even 10 seconds. During training at Athletes' Performance, the cold plunge is a vital step to maximizing recovery. The goal is for athletes to spend 1 to 10 minutes immersed in cold and then immediately jump into the hot tub (a pleasant 102 °F or 38.9 °C).

Scott

When I met Jogi in the cold plunge, I was curious about who he was. I observed that he was being whisked around Athletes' Performance like a VIP and knew that he wasn't simply another athlete being trained. When we got into the hot plunge (a much better place to hold a conversation), I asked him about his reason for being there. As Jogi told me about his father and his journey, I was taken aback. My father had also died too young, at 53 years old, and it was part of my motivation in always staying healthy (even in a highly hazardous occupation like firefighting).

When Jogi told me about his vision for Tignum, I felt an even bigger jolt. Not because we had just jumped back into the cold plunge, but because I was going down a similar path with my "Igniting Personal Excellence" program.

I'm not sure if it was Jogi's great vision, the similarity in our father's stories, our shared love for tennis, or if it was something much larger ... but when I went home that night I knew our meeting that day wasn't a coincidence. I knew that I would become a part of Tignum, and together, Jogi and I would create something that would make a profound difference in people's lives.

Tignum—A Collaboration With a Different Approach

From our initial concepts, we spent the next year developing what is now Tignum content. It is the collaborative effort of many talented people who all share a fundamental drive to assist leaders in achieving their full potential so they can expand their positive impact on their organization, their brands, their customers, and their families.

Tignum is an international team of high performance coaches and business consultants from various fields including organizational behavior, brain performance, leadership, innovation management, high performance medicine (western, eastern, holistic, and sports medicine), performance nutrition, performance movement, and performance recovery.

Since 2003, Tignum has worked with over 2,000 top executives (board members, CEOs, and senior leaders) from diverse companies in over 20 countries. Our clients include Fortune 500 companies such as IBM, Unilever, Novartis, GlaxoSmithKline, Accenture, DSM, and Adidas.

What Tignum Is / Not

Over the years we have had numerous conversations with CEOs, top executives, HR leaders, and even travelers sitting next to us on an airplane (a place where we have spent way too much time). As we describe Tignum in these conversations, we often get the response, "Oh, you guys are a health and wellness program."

We always bounce back with: "No, we are a company focused on developing high performance in business, and improving your health and wellness just happens to be a beneficial side effect." After further discussion, people always understand that what we do is definitely about improving performance, but for some reason it isn't always easy to quickly and succinctly paint the picture of our work.

Perhaps some of the comparisons our clients have shared with us will help you clearly see who we are.

Tignum is ...	... not
individualized	one-size-fits-all
an excuse annihilator	an enabler
a change catalyst	complacent
pragmatic and tangible	philosophical or theoretical
energizing	exhausting
a long-term solution	a quick fix
flexible	rigid
integrated (multidisciplinary)	uni-disciplinary
out-of-the-box thinking	status quo
thought and action provoking	knowledge dumping
a team builder	a team divider
an asset to an organization	a cost to an organization
what could be	**what is**

Our Mission

We have written this book to address the missing links in sustainable high performance leadership. In these tough times, too many leaders are simply focused on survival. We hope we have challenged you to shift your focus in order to discover the ways that you can increase your response-ability (ability to respond to high demands) and your perform-ability (ability to perform at your potential). We are passionate and committed to helping you build the capacity required to consistently perform at your best.

We invite you to become engaged in our process, which is designed to assist you in identifying current ineffective habits, developing more effective strategies, and implementing new high performance behaviors and routines. In our work, these strategies have been proven to be effective, simple, synergistic, and practical to fit the highly demanding lives of top performing leaders.

Above all, we hope to inspire you to develop and implement the strategies and habits necessary to perform at your best today, develop your potential for tomorrow, and get more out of everything you do every day.

www.tignum.com

Sink, Float, or Swim Acknowledgments

At this point, thanks are not enough for all the people who have personally and professionally influenced us. Throughout both of our lives, we have been blessed to have numerous people who have taught us, pushed us, coached us, loved us, and at times, kicked our butts. We are a product of all of you, and this book is a result of our experiences with all of you. Therefore, please know that it would take another entire book to properly thank you all, but since we are short on time, we hope these few pages will suffice.

It would be impossible to begin without thanking each other first. There are people you meet with whom you become instant friends, but we have become far more than that. So often, we have been in different countries only to wake up and find that we had both sent an e-mail to each other with the identical idea. These would have remained thoughts, but we always challenged each other to turn these ideas into reality. From the first day we met, we both shared a passion for making Tignum a special company, a unique project with far-reaching impact that inspires others to be their best. We have never had a doubt or faltered in our commitment to our four core values of fun, freedom, innovation, and impact.

At the end of every day, we can both say that we are better people for having met, and this book is one step in the dream we set out to fulfill. People say we fight like a married couple and we think like we share one brain, but we always push each other to be better, to make Tignum better, and to make our legacy an authentic one. Thanks for the thought-provoking discussions and amazing discoveries, and most of all, for so many fun matches on the tennis court.

We are forever grateful for Christine Buss. You fell out of the sky and helped immensely to bring our ideas together. You are a workhorse, and your incredible attention to detail and your resilience under our myriad demands made this book a reality.

Tignum would not be possible without our partners (and other founders) Pieter Christiaan van Oranje, Mark Verstegen, Dan Burns, and the entire Athletes' Performance family. Creating anything of significance is always the product of much brainstorming, lots of idea sharing, and a few favors to open some doors. Without every one of you, there would be no Tignum.

From the beginning, we have been fortunate to attract an extraordinarily talented team. Everything at Tignum, and especially this book, has been a team effort. Patti Milligan, Duncan Coombe, and Andre Hartwich—thanks so much for your unselfish sharing and giving from the start. You were not only patient; you always believed in our vision for Tignum and then did everything you could to make it come true. Without you, our Mindset, Nutrition, Movement, Recovery, and Benefit Attainment content would not be the world-class program that it has become. Patti, you are the best nutritionist we have ever met and without you, this book and Tignum would not be the same. Tanis Shelly, you have been a godsend. You are a terrier, willing to take on any task, and attack it with zeal. Dr. Lutz Graumann, Stefan Schaidnagel, Alexander Putz, Karen Arnold, and Adrianne Bowden—you are dedicated teammates and your support has helped make this book and Tignum a huge success. As we thank our Tignum team, we would be remiss if we didn't also send out a special thank you to Paul Preston and James Henderson. Both of you have taken us under your wing and passionately believed in the power of our work.

The design of a book is what makes the reader comfortable and open to the messages the words try to convey. Our designers Marko Puclin, Janine Nemec, and Achim Trumpfheller are awesome. Thanks so much for your creativity, your patience, and your hard work.

Finally, we would like to thank Sandy Ogg for having the trust to engage us in our first program. It was a real privilege to work with your team, and we are forever grateful for the opportunity to exceed your expectations.

Scott's Acknowledgements

I want to begin by thanking my wife Karen. Your belief in me and in Tignum has been amazing. Through all of my late nights, endless phone calls, miles of travel, and yes, even a few obsessions with perfection, you have supported me. Your patience with my last minute edits and impossible deadlines has been angelic. I also want to thank Kristina and Daniel. You are my inspiration to achieve my potential, and I hope to become worthy of being called your dad. And, thanks to Boozer (our Queensland Heeler) for keeping me company on so many late nights of writing.

When I think of the people who have influenced me and made an impact on my life, I have to put Chief Alan Brunacini at the top. You have been an inspiration, a motivator, and a father figure to me. Your belief in me and your openness to all of my wild ideas helped me form my opinions and grow into the person that I am today. You are not only the greatest Fire Chief there ever was, you are the greatest mentor. Thank you for everything.

I want to thank my mom (Deanne Lange) and my father (Izzy Peltin). Mom, your work ethic and no-nonsense approach to life has helped shape me, and always enabled me to move from knowing to doing. You taught me how important it is to think for myself, develop my own opinions, and speak up. Dad, I know you never got to see who I have become as a man, but you were my first coach and gave me the coaching gene in my DNA. You left us too early, and it is this fact that has driven me to assist our clients in changing their habits. I also want to thank my in-laws, Gerry and Sheila Chaney, for all of your help and support. The 5:30 a.m. chats, the critical review of the chapters, your book and article reviews, and of course, the talks at the BBQ all helped tremendously.

Finally, I have to say that much of what I have learned has been through the projects I have been a part of and the experiences I have had as a coach and on the Phoenix Fire Department. I would like to thank my friends Tom and Rhonda Hascall, Wendy Ballas, Derek Alkonis, Jeff Case, Warren Bowden, Joe Bledsoe, Olivia Templeton, and Bill Whitaker. You all have a special place in my heart and in my development, and I thank you all for your friendship and support. Lastly, I want to thank Deby and Brad Harper for opening my eyes to the DISC Profile System and expanding my horizons. Deby, you are way ahead of your time.

Jogi's Acknowledgements

My biggest thank you goes to my wife Doris. You are my greatest supporter. Thanks so much for believing in me and sharing my passion for Tignum. Your critical questions, creative input, and dedication to quality brought us to another level. Thanks also for your patience while I was on the phone with Scott on so many nights and weekends.

I want to thank my parents Inge and Hermann Rippel for showing me the world of entrepreneurship and for always letting me go my way. Thanks, Dad, for the inspiring talks we had during your cancer journey. You left us way too early, but with the creation of Tignum, your death has brought great meaning. Every person we impact, we impact because of you.

Also, a big thank you to my wonderful friends Thomas Mayer and Yvonne Baur. You always believed in my crazy ideas. Thanks for making me a part of your family and for your endless hours of consulting.

The Tignum idea actually started at the IMD business school in Lausanne, Switzerland. Thanks to Tanja and Martijn Hol (and for all the nights at the Hol Hilton) and Katis and Fred Bergegard for all your support, challenging questions, and strategic input. Thanks also to my IMD buddies Bogdan Madzar, Mirko and Helen Giacomo, and Michelle Burke who worked with me on the cancer project. A warm hug to Rosie Daniels who is a role model that truly makes a difference and to Sean Meehan for my first opportunity to lecture at IMD.

Many good friends supported me in the creation and development of Tignum. Giorgio Bottega—your passion for sustainability and your architecture is beyond description. You are a true visionary. I promise we will build a Tignum facility soon. Andre Steck—our dream lawyer—thanks for your remarkable energy and brilliant input. Roger Kehl, my old school friend, thank you for always searching for an open door for us. Jürgen Dürr, Mr. Blackroll—thanks for your continual and sound input. Jacek Jonczyk—your digital input made a difference and brought us many compliments. Thank you all for your friendship.

Notes and References

Prologue

Interview with former President Bill Clinton: *The Role of a Former President,*
November 2008, television program, CNN's Talk Asia, Japan.

Chapter One

Burnout rates: G. K. Kulkarni, "Burnout," *Indian Journal of Occupational and Environmental Medicine,*
October 2006, pp. 3-4.

Cost of presenteeism: Paul Hemp, "Presenteeism—At Work But Out of It," *Harvard Business Review,*
October 2004, p. 3.

Financial Times article: Donald Sull, "Why the Worst Times Can Also Be the Best of Times,"
Financial Times, December 1, 2008, p. 1.

Martin Luther King Jr. quote: Martin Luther King, Jr., *Strength to Love* (First Fortress Press, 1981), p.15.

Study by Accenture: *Individual Investors Enthusiastic About Stock Market but Lack Capabilities
to Measure Companies' True Value and Growth Prospects, Accenture Study Finds,*
March 2006, press release, Accenture, US, viewed October 28, 2008,
<http://newsroom.accenture.com/article_display.cfm?article_id=4317>.

Dr. Brian Sutton-Smith quote: Bernie DeKoven, *The Opposite of Play,* March 2007, online article,
DeepFUN, US, viewed July 12, 2008, <http://www.deepfun.com/2007/03/opposite-of-play.html>.

Chapter Two

Jim Collins interview: Alan M. Webber, *Good Questions, Great Answers,* December 2007,
web interview, Fast Company, US, viewed December 13, 2008,
<http://www.fastcompany.com/articles/2001/09/collins.html?page=0%2C0>.

Matthias Malessa interview: *Giving 110%: Our Efforts to be a Responsible Business in 2007,*
corporate review, adidas Group, Germany, viewed November 21, 2008,
<http://www.corporateregister.com/a10723/AdidasGro7rev-csr-de.pdf>.

Chapter Three

Jack Welch quote: Jack Welch, *Are Leaders Born or Made?*, December 2005, web blog, The Welch Way, US, viewed June 22, 2008,
<http://www.welchway.com/Management/Leadership/What-Makes-a-Leader/Are-Leaders-Born-or-Made.aspx>.

Michael Jordan quote: Phil Gordon, *Still No Bracelet,* August 16, 2007, online article, ESPN, US, viewed February 2, 2009, <http://sports.espn.go.com/espn/print?id=2977179&type=story>.

Brain performance and potential: Carla J. Shatz, "The Developing Brain," *The Scientific American Book of the Brain* (Scientific American, 1993), p. 3.

Brain statistics: Daniel Drubach, *The Brain Explained* (Prentice Hall, 1999), pp. 36-37.

Adequate sleep: Printed with permission of Dr. Mark Mahowald, MD, Director of the Minnesota Regional Sleep Disorders Center. For additional information,
see <http://www.hcmc.org/medical%20expert%20bios/mahowaldmark.htm >.

Dan Ephron, *Singing for Your Sleep,* October 30, 2006, online article, *Newsweek,* US, viewed August 22, 2008, <http://www.newsweek.com/id/45162>.

Stress and the brain: Robert Sapolsky, *Why Zebras Don't Get Ulcers* (Henry Holt and Company, 2004), pp. 202-225.

Omega-3 fatty acids research: Patricia E. Wainwright, "Omega-3 Fatty Acids and the Brain," *Nutrition,* Nov/Dec 1991, pp. 443-446.

Irwin H. Rosenberg, "Rethinking Brain Food." *American Journal of Clinical Nutrition.* November 2007, pp. 1259-1260.

Brain cells and aging: Dr. Daniel Amen, *Cool Brain Facts,* online article, Amen Clinics, US, viewed January 2, 2009, <http://www.amenclinics.com/brain-science/cool-brain-science/cool-brain-facts/>.

Right-brain thinking: Daniel Pink, *A Whole New Mind: Moving from the Information Age to the Conceptual Age* (The Penguin Group, 2005), p. 25.

Daniel Pink, *A Whole New Mind: Why Right-Brainers Will Rule the Future,* (Berkley Pub Group, 2006).

Whole-brain thinking: Chris McManus, *Right Hand, Left Hand: The Origins of Asymmetry in Brains, Bodies, Atoms and Cultures* (Harvard University Press, 2004), pp. 183-184.

Business and karaoke: Kjell Nordström, *DSM Internal High Performance Conference,* keynote address, Düsseldorf, Germany, March 8, 2007.

Chapter Four

Costs of stress: *What Is Burn-out and Depression?*, 2008, online article, Douglas Institute, Canada, viewed January 4, 2009, <http://burnout.douglas.qc.ca/burn-out/facts-and-figures.html>.

Prepared by Cardiff University and Queen Mary University of London for the Health and Safety Executive, "Ethnicity, Work Characteristics, Stress and Health," 2005, pp. 6-8.

Burnout study: "Burnout Britain: Raising the Alarm for Employers," *A Hudson Report*, 2005, pp. 2-3.

Burnout cycle: Ulrich Kraft, "Burned Out," *Scientific American Mind*, June 2006, pp. 28-33.

Tension myositis syndrome: John Sarno, *The Mindbody Prescription: Healing the Body, Healing the Pain* (Warner Books, 1999).

Joe Robinson quote: Joe Robinson, *Work to Live: The Guide to Getting a Life* (Perigee, 2003), p. 30.

Definition of presenteeism: Paul Hemp, "Presenteeism—At Work But Out of It," *Harvard Business Review*, October 2004, pp. 3-4.

Unproductive hours chart: adapted from original by Cornell University Institute for Health and Productivity Studies (IHPS), CDC-NIOSH Steps to a Healthier U.S. Workforce Symposium, October 26-28, 2004, Washington, DC.

Lockheed Martin study: Paul Hemp, "Presenteeism—At Work But Out of It," *Harvard Business Review*, October 2004, p. 6.

Leadership and mindlessness: Richard E. Boyatzis and Annie McKee, *Resonant Leadership: Renewing Yourself and Connecting with Others Through Mindfulness, Hope, and Compassion* (Harvard Business School Publishing, 2005), p. 130.

C. K. Prahalad: Personal interview with Tignum, January 19, 2009.

Trends for investment groups: Yuval Rosenburg, "Measured Progress," *Fast Company*, April 2007.

R. Paul Herman: Personal interview with Tignum. December 18, 2008.

Steve Jobs' health: Jessica Mintz, "Apple Shares Fall on Steve Jobs Health News," *The Huffington Post*, January 15, 2009.

Peter Drucker quote: Robert K. Cooper, "Excelling Under Pressure: Increasing Your Energy for Leadership and Innovation in a World of Stress, Change and Unprecedented Opportunities," *Strategy and Leadership*, January 2001, p. 15.

Study of high-earners and work: Sylvia Ann Hewlett and Carolyn Buck Luce, "Extreme Jobs: The Dangerous Allure of the 70-Hour Workweek," *Harvard Business Review*, December 2007, pp. 62-64.

Chapter Five

Interruption science: BusinessWeek Video 2008, *Maggie Jackson's book Distracted,*
online Businessweek Video Library, US, viewed June 11, 2008, <http://feedroom.businessweek.com/>.

E-mail and web statistics: *The World Wide Web Is One Big Machine,* August 4, 2008, online article
with statistics from Kevin Kelly of Wired Magazine, US, viewed November 6, 2008,
<http://www.sayyestono.org/DasBlog/PermaLink,guid,f2eb3d19-12d8-4b3e-9e7b-2adaeaa4b1ae.aspx>.

1800s health book: Thomas John Graham, *Sure Methods to Improving Health and Prolonging Life*
(London, 1828).

Chapter Six

Common self-talk traps: Betsy Shoenfelt, *Self-Talk: The Power of Positive Thinking,*
online article, Department of Psychology, Western Kentucky University, US, viewed February 23, 2009,
<http://edtech.tph.wku.edu/~bshoenfe/mentalskillsselftalk.htm>.

Metacognition and performance: Geoff Colvin, *Talent is Overrated: What Really Separates World-
Class Performers from Everybody Else* (Tantor Media, 2008), p. 11.

Tiger Woods reviews and practice: *Tiger – The Authorized DVD Collection,* DVD,
Buena Vista Home Entertainment, 2004.

Tiger Woods record: Tiger Woods Official Website, 2009, Tiger Woods, US, viewed January 5, 2009,
<http://www.tigerwoods.com>.

Hardiness study: S. C. Kobasa, "Stressful Life Events, Personality, and Health: An Inquiry into
Hardiness," *Journal of Personality and Social Psychology,* January 1979, pp. 1-11.

The strengths revolution: Printed with permission from Marcus Buckingham.
For additional information, see <http://www.marcusbuckingham.com>.

Chapter Seven

Tiger Woods Quote: *Tiger – The Authorized DVD Collection,* DVD, Buena Vista Home Entertainment,
2004.

Betancourt and Mindset: *Free at Last: Columbian Hostage One-On-One,* July 2008,
television program, NBC Today Show, US.

Chapter Eight

Carlo Petrini and the slow food movement: Carlo Petrini, *Slow Food Nation: Why Our Food Should be Good, Clean and Fair* (Rizzoli Ex Libris, 2007).

Changing British school menus: *The Naked Chef: Series 1-3,* DVD, 2006, BBC Series, Universal Pictures, produced by Kent Weed.

Protein and immunity: Bill Campbell et al, "International Society of Sports Nutrition Position Stand: Protein and Exercise," *Journal of International Society of Sports Nutrition,* 4:8, 2007.

W. M. Rand et al, "Meta-Analysis of Nitrogen Balance Studies for Estimating Protein Requirements in Healthy Adults," *American Journal of Clinical Nutrition,* January 2003, pp. 109-127.

Nutrition and brain functioning: Amen Clinics, Dr. Daniel Amen, US, viewed July 23, 2008, ⟨http://www.amenclinics.com/⟩.

Prisoner and fish oil study: Jeremy Laurance, "Prison Study to Investigate Link Between Junk Food and Violence," *The Independent,* January 2008.

Impact of food and physiologic hunger: *Food and Eating Module: American Time Use Survey,* USDA Study, 2003.

Slow Food, Slow Food USA, 2008, viewed June 9, 2008, ⟨http://www.slowfoodusa.org⟩.

The Weston A. Price Foundation for Wise Traditions, US, viewed May 29, 2008, ⟨http://westonaprice.org/⟩.

Digestive enzymes: Melvin R. Werbach, MD, *Nutritional Influences on Illness* (Third Line Press, 1993).

Childhood obesity: *Healthy Youth! Childhood Obesity,* October 2008, online article and resources, CDC: National Center for Chronic Disease Prevention and Health Promotion, US, viewed September 5, 2008, ⟨http://www.cdc.gov/HealthyYouth/obesity/index.htm⟩.

Eating and stress: Dr. Jonathan Collin, MD, Editor-in-Chief, *Townsend Letter for Doctors and Patients,* 2004.

Melvin R. Werbach, MD, *Nutritional Influences on Illness* (Third Line Press, 1993).

Michael Cutler, MD, *The Untold Truth Series,* Wasatch Research Institute, 2004.

Eating and travel: Food Standards Agency, 2009, Food Standards, UK, viewed October 23, 2008, ⟨http://www.food.gov.uk/⟩.

Water and dehydration: M.-M. G. Wilson, "Impaired Cognitive Function and Mental Performance in Mild Dehydration," *European Journal of Clinical Nutrition,* December 2003.

P. J. Rogers et al, "A Drink of Water Can Improve or Impair Mental Performance Depending on Small Differences in Thirst, *Appetite,* (36), 2001, pp. 57-58.

S. M. Kleiner, "Water: An Essential But Overlooked Nutrient," *Journal of the American Dietetic Association,* February 1999, pp. 200-206.

Hydrated and dehydrated brain photos: Photographs provided by Dr. Daniel Amen from Amen Clinics, Inc. For additional information, see <http://www.amenclinics.com/>.

Hydration measures: Mayo Clinic Staff, *Water: How Much Should You Drink Every Day?,* online article, April 2008, Mayo Foundation for Medical Education and Research (MFMER), US, viewed December 18, 2008, <http://www.mayoclinic.com/print/water/NU00283/METHOD=print>.

Benefits of performance drinks: K. L. Tucker et al, "Colas, But Not Other Carbonated Beverages, Are Associated with Low Bone Mineral Density in Older Women: The Framingham Osteoporosis Study," *American Journal of Clinical Nutrition,* October 2006, pp. 936-942.

K. Rezai-Zadeh et al, "Green Tea Epigallocatechin-3-gallate (EGCG) Reduces beta-amyloid Mediated Cognitive Impairment and Modulates Tau Pathology in Alzheimer Transgenic Mice, *Brain Research,* June 2008, pp. 177-187.

Qi Dai, MD, Phd, et al, "Fruit and Vegetable Juices and Alzheimer's Disease: The Kame Project," *The American Journal of Medicine,* September 2006, pp. 751-759.

R. Cuomo et al, "Effects of Carbonated Water on Dyspepsia and Constipation," *European Journal of Gastroeneterology and Hepatology,* 14 (9), 2002.

S. Schoppen et al, "A Sodium Rich Carbonated Mineral Water Reduces Cardiovascular Risk in Postmenopausal Women," *The Journal of Nutrition,* May 2004, pp. 1058-1063.

University of Oxford, "Chocolate, Wine and Tea Improve Brain Performance," *ScienceDaily,* December 2008.

Coffee, performance, and information: C. F. Brice and A. P. Smith, "Effects of Caffeine on Mood and Performance: A Study of Realistic Consumption," *Psychopharmacology,* 164, 2002, pp. 188-192.

M. C. Cornelis et al, "Coffee, CYP1A2 Genotype, and Risk of Myocardial Infarction," *The Journal of the American Medical Association,* (295), 2006, pp.1135-1141.

M. H. Bonnet and D.L. Arand, "The Use of Prophylactic Naps and Caffeine to Maintain Performance During a Continuous Operation," *Ergonomics,* 37(6), 1994, pp.1009-1020.

National Coffee Association, 2009, Coffee Science Source, US, viewed June 24, 2008, <http://www.coffeescience.org/>.

Free radicals: *Understanding Free Radicals and Antioxidants,* 2009, online article, Health Check Systems, US, viewed November 21, 2008, <http://www.healthchecksystems.com/antioxid.htm>.

Chapter Nine

Blood glucose fluctuations: *American Association Scientific Sessions 2007,* Orange County Convention Center, Orlando, Florida, Nov 4-7, 2007.

M. P. Mattson and R. Wan, "Beneficial Effects of Intermittent Fasting and Caloric Restriction on the Cardiovascular and Cerebrovascular Systems," *Journal of Nutrition Biochemistry,* March 2005, pp. 129-137.

R. M. Anson et al, "Intermittent Fasting Dissociates Beneficial Effects of Dietary Restriction on Glucose Metabolism and Neuronal Resistance to Injury from Calorie Intake," *Proceedings of the National Academy of Sciences,* May 2003, pp. 6216-6220.

Blood glucose and performance: Research from Paul E. Gold, PhD, Professor of Psychology, University of Illinois at Urbana-Champaign. For additional information, see <http://www.psych.uiuc.edu/people/showprofile.php?id=51>.

Retention tests and blood glucose: R. Gruetter et al, "Steady-State Cerebral Glucose Concentrations and Transport in the Human Brain," *Journal of Neurochemistry,* (70)1, 1998, pp. 397-408.

Skipping meals and blood glucose: e! Science News, 2009, Eureka! Science News, USA, viewed July 9, 2008, <http://esciencenews.com/>.

Poor sleep and blood glucose: S. Seicean et al, "Sleep-Disordered Breathing and Impaired Glucose Metabolism in Normal-Weight and Overweight/Obese Individuals: The Sleep Heart Health Study," *Diabetes Care,* May 2008, pp. 1001-1006.

Nuts research: D. Jenkins et al, "Almonds Decrease Postprandial Glycemia, Insulinemia, and Oxidative Damage in Healthy Individuals," *The Journal of Nutrition,* December 2006, p. 2987-2992.

E. Huskisson, S. Maggini, and M. Ruf, "The Influence of Micronutrients on Cognitive Function and Performance," *The Journal of International Medical Research,* 35(1), 2007, pp. 1-19.

M. F. Muldoon, S. Conklin, C. M. Ryan, J. Yao, J. Hibbeln, and S. B. Manuck, "Cognitive Function and Omega-6 and Omega-3 Fatty Acid Balance," *American Psychosomatic Society Annual Meeting,* March 2007, Budapest, Hungary, abstract.

R. K. McNamara and S. E. Carlson, "Role of Omega-3 Fatty Acids in Brain Development and Function: Potential Implications for the Pathogenesis and Prevention of Psychopathology," *Prostaglandins Leukotrienes and Essential Fatty Acids,* October 2006, pp. 329-349.

S. M. Conklin, J. I. Harris, S. B. Manuck, et al, "Serum Omega-3 Fatty Acids Are Associated With Variation in Mood, Personality and Behavior in Hypercholesterolemic Community Volunteers," *Psychiatry Research,* July 30, 2007, pp. 1-10.

S. M. Conklin, P. J. Gianaros, S. M. Brown, et al, "Long-Chain Omega-3 Fatty Acid Intake Is Associated Positively with Corticolimbic Gray Matter Volume in Healthy Adults," *Neuroscience Letters,* June 2007, pp. 209-212.

S. M. Conklin, S. B. Manuck, J. K. Yao, J. R. Hibbeln, J. D. Flory, and M. F. Muldoon, "Serum Phospholipid Polyunsaturated Fatty Acids Are Associated With Mood, Behavior and Personality in Healthy Community Adults," *American Psychosomatic Society Annual Meeting,* March 2007, Budapest, Hungary, abstract 1718.

Nutrient intake: W. Broekmans et al, TNO Nutrition and Food Research and TNOWU Centre for Micronutrient Research, The Netherlands.

Formula for nutrient dense diet: Joel Fuhrman, MD, *Eat to Live: The Revolutionary Formula for Fast and Sustained Weight Loss* (Little, Brown and Company, 2003), p. 7.

Tignum Color Code Body: Developed by Tignum Director of Nutrition Patti Milligan. Codes are based upon meta-anlaysis studies, major reports on pigments and their physiologic functionality. Various disciplines of phytochemical, nutritional, biochemical, and functional food research, including:

ORAC work by Dr. Bruce Ames, ‹http://www.ars.usda.gov/is/AR/archive/feb99/aging0299.htm›.

Birgit Holst and Gary Williamson, "Nutrients and Phytochemicals: From Bioavailability to Bioefficacy Beyond Antioxidants," *Current Opinion in Biotechnology,* April 2008, pp. 73-82.

C. Gemma et al, "Diets Enriched in Foods with High Antioxidant Activity Reverse Age-Induced Decreases In Cerebellar A-adrenergic Function and Increases in Pro-inflammatory Cytokines," *Journal of Neuroscience,* July 2002, pp. 6114-6120.

G. Cao et al, "Hyperoxia-Induced Changes in Antioxidant Capacity and the Effect of Dietary Antioxidants," *Journal of Applied Physiology,* June 1999, pp. 1817-1822.

Institut Scientifique et Technique de la Nutrition et de l'Alimentation, Paris, France.

Jeanelle Boyer and Rui Hai Liu, "Apple Phytochemicals and Their Health Benefits," *Nutrition Journal,* 3:5, 2004.

Judy McBride, USDA, Agricultural Research Service, August 9, 1999.

Life Extension Foundation research at ‹www.lef.org›.

N. Darmon et al, "A Nutrient Density Standard for Vegetables and Fruits: Nutrients Per Calorie and Nutrients Per Unit Cost," *Journal of the American Dietetic Association,* December 2005, pp. 1881-1887.

Ronald Prior, James Joseph, Guohua Cao, Barbara Shukitt-Hale, Jean Mayer, USDA Human Nutrition Research Center on Aging, Tufts University, Boston, Massachusetts.

Chapter Ten

Foods and drinks for detoxification: "Symposium on Phytochemicals: Biochemistry and Physiology American Society for Nutritional Sciences," *Journal of Nutrition,* 129, 1999, pp. 7565-7575.

Calories for nutrient needs: S. B. Eaton and M. J. Konner, "Paleolithic Nutrition Revisted: A Twelve-Year Retrospection on Its Nature and Implications," *European Journal of Clinical Nutrition,* 51, 1991, pp. 207-216.

S. Boyd Eaton, MD, Marjorie Shostak, and Melvin Konner, *The Paleolithic Prescription: A Program of Diet & Exercise and a Design for Living* (Harpercollins, 1988).

Ayurveda: The National Institute of Ayurvedic Medicine, 2008, US, Scott Gerson, MD, viewed June 4, 2008,<http://niam.com>.

Variation in body chemistry: Roger J. Williams, PhD, *Biochemical Individuality: Key to Understanding What Shapes Your Health* (Keats Publishing, 1998).

Diet-related diseases: William L. Wolcott and Trish Fahey, *The Metabolic Typing Diet: Customize Your Diet to Your Own Unique & Ever Changing Nutritional Needs* (Bantam Books, 2002).

Chapter Eleven

Exercise and health: American Association for Cancer Research, *Exercise and Rest Reduce Cancer Risk,* November 2008, online article, ScienceDaily, US, viewed December 3, 2008, <http://www.sciencedaily.com/releases/2008/11/081117153154.htm>.

Associated Press, *Walking and Longevity Study: Exercise Can Add 3 Years to Life Expectancy,* 2005, online article, MSNBC, US, viewed July 18, 2008, <http://www.msnbc.msn.com/id/10039577/>.

Benefits of Exercise in Cancer Care, 2006, online article, ExerciseWorks of Boston, US, viewed August 15, 2008, <http://www.bostonexerciseworks.com/CancerWellnessProgram/exercise.html>.

Exercise 'Prevents and Treats' Cancer, May 2008, online article, NHS Choices, England, viewed June 3, 2008, <http://www.nhs.uk/news/2008/05May/Pages/Exercisepreventsandtreatscancer.aspx>.

Exercise and Alzheimer's disease: John Ratey, Spark: *The Revolutionary New Science of Exercise and the Brain* (Little, Brown and Company, 2008).

Movement, balance, and brain integration: The Brain Muscle Workout 2007, The Brain Muscle Workout Fitness Program, US, viewed June 23, 2008, <http://www.thebrainmuscleworkout.com>.

PBS – Scientific American Frontiers, 2002, *Brainy Putting,* online video, viewed August 12, 2008, <http://www.pbs.org/saf/1206/video/watchonline.htm>.

Patterns of Movement: Juan Carlos Santana, *Functional Training: Breaking the Bonds of Traditionalism* (Juan Carlos Santana, 2000).

Good Movement patterns: Gray Cook, *Athletic Body in Balance* (Human Kinetics, 2003).

Posture graphic: Adapted from graphic developed by Mark Verstegen, Athletes' Performance, Tempe, Arizona. For additional information, see <http://www.athletesperformance.com/>.

Chapter Twelve

ESD training program: Athletes' Performance, Tempe, Arizona. For additional information, see <http://www.athletesperformance.com/>.

VO2 Max: Elizabeth Quinn, *VO2 Max Measures Aerobic Fitness and Maximal Oxygen Uptake,* June 2008, online article, About.com: Sports Medicine, viewed July 8, 2008, <http://sportsmedicine.about.com/od/anatomyandphysiology/a/VO2_max.htm>.

Exercise and muscle mass: ACE, 2009, American Council on Exercise, US, viewed August 15, 2008, <http://www.acefitness.org/>.

Chapter Thirteen

Selye's research on stress: Hans Seyle, *Stress Without Distress* (New Amer Library, 1991).

Hans Selye, *The Nature of Stress,* online article, International Center for Nutritional Research, Inc., US, viewed July 23, 2008, <http://www.icnr.com/articles/thenatureofstress.html>.

Hans Seyle, *The Stress of Life* (McGraw-Hill, 1978).

Stress and flow: Mihály Csíkszentmihályi. *Flow: The Psychology of Optimal Experience* (HarperPerennial, 1990).

Chapter Fourteen

Sleep research: William C. Dement and C. Vaughan, *The Promise of Sleep: A Pioneer in Sleep Medicine Explores the Vital Connection Between Health, Happiness, and a Good Night's Sleep* (Bantam Dell Publishing Group, 1999).

Sleep Facts and Stats, National Sleep Foundation, US, viewed November 22, 2008, <http://www.sleepfoundation.org/site/c.huIXKjMOIxF/b.2419253/k.7989/Sleep_Facts_and_Stats.htm>.

Sleep and travel: *Business Travel Statistics,* British Airways July 2005 statistics, Entrepreneur, US, viewed September 12, 2008, <http://www.entrepreneur.com/encyclopedia/statistics/article82014.html>.

US Military studies on power naps: E. Williams, et al, "Human Performance,"
Internal Government Report, unclassified, JSR-07-625, March 2008.

NASA research on naps: Michael B. Mann, NASA Study, Office of Aero-Space Technology National
Aeronautics and Space Administration, August 3, 1999.

Tom Peters quote: Printed with permission of Tom Peters. For additional information, see
<http://www.tompeters.com>.

Laughter and Recovery: L. S. Berk, D. L. Felten, S. A. Tan, B. B. Bittman, J. Westengard,
"Modulation of Neuroimmune Parameters During the Eustress of Humor-Associated Mirthful Laughter,"
Alternative Therapies in Health and Medicine, March 2001.

M. P. Bennett, C. Lengacher, "Humor and Laughter May Influence Health: III. Laughter and Health
Outcomes," *Evidence-Based Complementary and Alternative Medicine,* March 2008, pp 37-40.

M. P. Bennett, J. M. Zeller, L. Rosenberg, J. McCann, "The Effect of Mirthful Laughter on Stress and
Natural Killer Cell Activity," *Alternative Therapies in Health and Medicine,* March – April 2003.

N. Skinner, N. Brewer, "The Dynamics of Threat and Challenge Appraisals Prior to Stressful
Achievement Events," *Journal of Personality and Social Psychology,* September 2002.

Humor in the workplace: University of Missouri-Columbia, *Light Humor in the Workplace Is a Good
Thing, Review Shows,* November 2007, online article, ScienceDaily, US, viewed May 5, 2008,
<http://www.sciencedaily.com¬ /releases/2007/10/071031130917.htm>.

Laughter and diabetes study: T. Hayashi, S. Tsujii, et al, "Laughter Up-Regulates the Genes Related
to NK Cell Activity in Diabetes," *Biomedical Research,* December 2007, pp. 281-285.

Paul Ekman on facial expressions: Malcolm Gladwell, *Blink: The Power of Thinking Without Thinking*
(Little, Brown and Company, 2005), pp. 206-208.

Chapter Sixteen

Heart attacks and change: Alan Deutschman, "Change or Die," *Fast Company,* May 2005.

Tignum Benefit Attainment Process: Developed with Duncan Coombe, an organizational behavior
expert and leadership consultant from Case Western University.

John Kotter on behavior change: Alan Deutschman, "Change or Die," *Fast Company,* May 2005, p. 54.

Quitting and the dip: Seth Godin, *The Dip: A Little Book That Teaches You When to Quit (and When
to Stick)* (Penguin Books, 2007), p. 33.

Performance and goal setting: Geoff Colvin, *Talent is Overrated: What Really Separates World-Class
Performers From Everybody Else* (Tantor Media, 2008).

Chapter Seventeen

Collaboration in business: Ellen McGirt, "How Cisco's CEO John Chambers is Turning the Tech Giant Socialist," *Fast Company*, December 2008.

Clive Woodward and Mindset: Clive Woodward, *Winning!: The Story of England's Rise to Rugby World Cup Glory* (Hodder & Stoughton Ltd, 2005).

Anne Mulcahy and Mindset: Bill George, "America's Best Leaders: Anne Mulcahy, Xerox CEO," *US News and World Report*, November 2008.

Climbing stairs saves energy: *How Much Energy Does It Take to Use an Elevator for One Floor or How Much Money Does It Cost to Use an Elevator Lift for One Floor?* WikiAnswers, viewed December 5, 2008, <http://wiki.answers.com/Q/>.

Climbing stairs burns calories: *How to Estimate the Number of Calories You Burn Walking Up the Stairs,* eHow, viewed December 5, 2008, <http://ehow.com/how_4670381>.

Walking workstation study: *"Office of the Future" Environment Study,* August 2008, online article, Mayo Clinic, US, viewed December 5, 2008, <http://www.mayoclinic.org/news2008-rst/4924.html>.

Reduction in drag: Edmund Burke, *High-Tech Cycling* (Human Kinetics, 1996).

Chapter Eighteen

Business suicide: C.K. Prahalad, Personal interview with Tignum, January 19, 2009.

Bernhard Lobmueller on cuts: Personal interview with Tignum, January 13, 2009.

Measuring ROI: John W. Boudreau and Peter M. Ramstad, *Beyond HR: The New Science of Human Capital* (Harvard Business School Publishing Corporation, 2007).

Chapter Nineteen

Rita McGrath's view: Personal interview with Tignum, February 26, 2009.

Investing in high performance companies: Printed with permission from Kurt Ehmann, Financial Advisor for Financial Network, Los Angeles, California.

Employment trends: Matthew Guthridge, Asmus B. Komm, and Emily Lawson, "Making Talent a Strategic Priority," *The McKinsey Quarterly*, January 2008, pp. 50-59.

John Maxwell quote: Printed with permission from John Maxwell. For additional information, see <www.johnmaxwell.com>.

Notes